THE DRIFTWOOD DRAGON

C000066355

Dru's surprise at finding that Locke Matthews' real character was quite different from his *Ramage* image, soon became love for the tender and vulnerable man still haunted by dreams of Eva. But the dark held a real threat for them both . . .

Books you will enjoy
by ANN CHARLTON

NO LAST SONG

Ford Barron was, with good reason, highly suspicious of Briony Wilde. So when she went to work for his aunt, the sparks flew. Which was fine with Briony—until she found herself wanting something more . . .

WINTER SUN, SUMMER RAIN

Her relationship with ex-tennis champion Luke Harrow was too good to be true, thought Lacey as she ran up the stairs to her bedroom. And it was then that his mother appeared, and told her just how much truth there was in what Luke had said to her . . .

AN IRRESISTIBLE FORCE

As far as Fairlie was concerned, the irresistible force of Carson Tate's charm had met an immovable object. Even if he and his demolition crew seemed to hold all the cards . . .

THE DRIFTWOOD DRAGON

BY
ANN CHARLTON

MILLS & BOON LIMITED
15–16 BROOK'S MEWS
LONDON W1A 1DR

First published in Great Britain 1985 by Mills & Boon Limited

© Ann Charlton 1985

*Australian copyright 1985
Philippine copyright 1985
This edition 1985*

ISBN 0 263 75202 X

*Set in Monophoto Plantin 10 on 11 pt.
01–1185 – 55115*

Made and printed in Great Britain by Richard Clay (The Chaucer Press) Ltd, Bungay, Suffolk

CHAPTER ONE

IT was years since Dru had been afraid of the dark. Even the dark in this darkest hallway where it dodged around a corner to the staircase. As a child she'd always held her breath when she came to its end, imagining nameless night horrors waiting around the bend. The moment of truth had always come when she had to slide her hand around the corner to the light switch. She had to press it quickly or something horrible would get her. In her child's mind it had been as certain as the fact that pavement cracks had to be avoided at all costs. The switching on of the light had been the signal that would send the monsters with the clawed, gruesome hands and clanking chains shrivelling into no-man's land until next time.

Whatever had roused her had got her up and to this corner without turning on the wan hall light. She stood there, almost as reluctant as she'd been as a child to put her hand around the wall edge to turn on the stair light. It was nothing. She listened. Only the hush and crash of the ocean that had finally hypnotised her into half-sleep on this third night. Nothing. The stairs creaked. That didn't mean a thing. The holiday house had fallen into picturesque disrepair. Almost everything about it creaked, groaned or needed painting. She decided to go back to bed.

Then she heard the tiny clink of metal. Old images of chain-draped creatures flashed through a sleep starved mind and Dru froze in the dark, prey again to the old panic. Her hand went to the light switch. Fumbling, she found the cold plastic in the dark. The back of her neck tingled, and she held her breath to listen. There was something—something . . .

Something warm squeezed her fingers.

'Ssssh.'

The sound raised the hair on her neck. Dru screamed the scream that had been ready for just this when she was eight. Again a hiss of sound came close to her. The thing closed about her, practically lifting her off her feet and smothering her shrill cry. She fought. Her elbows struck something warm and solid and there was a grunting noise. Tight, thick fur brushed at her bare neck and her skin crawled. Whatever was over her mouth smelled of oil and hide. She tore at it and her fingers touched several hard, cold protuberances that brought another scream up from her diaphragm. Claws.

Outside she heard the sound of a car and the normality of it made her struggles wilder. She threw her body sideways and nearly broke loose but she was caught from behind.

'For Pete's sake, Shelley, be quiet. It's me,' a voice hissed in her ear and the human sound of it stilled her for a moment. Then there were sounds of people outside. More voices floated up to Dru like something out of a dream. That was it—a dream. She was asleep.

'You can't be serious. He wouldn't be seen dead in a place like this.'

'I thought I saw him turn in this direction——'

'Come on—the place is a shack, almost falling down.'

'Yeah, I guess you're right. He'll be heading for one of the high rise places further up the coast—hell! Talk about a needle in a haystack . . .' The voices faded.

A dream, Dru insisted. It must be. She'd finally got to sleep after nights of wakefulness and this was what she got. But the close warmth of the man seemed real enough—so did the hand over her mouth. Dru began to struggle again.

'Darling—shut *up*,' he whispered and kept her gagged until the car doors slammed. A deep sigh left the man. The warmth of it gusted past Dru's ear. The car growled away again on the unsurfaced road and as the hand slid from her mouth Dru yelped.

'Help—help—you get away from me——' This last as he let her go then came after her as she shrank back against the wall. He was a dark grey shape on a pitch background. 'Don't you touch me again—you get out of here, do you hear me——' her voice began to rise, 'I don't care if you're a monster or not——'

He found the switch. Her voice cut off instantly. Reality returned with the light that wanly revealed the familiar landing walls and the narrow stairs, that sloped off to the lower floor. And the man. Dru stared at him. He was tall and broad—his hair a dark, reddish brown as far as she could tell, and mussed. He wore a thigh length jacket with a sheepskin collar and she remembered its animal feel against her bare skin. Trousers, long boots and leather gloves that had small metal studs on the backs. Claws, she had thought in her idiotic half-sleep. There was something menacing about the way he removed the gauntlets and slapped them lightly against his arm. He came closer. His fine brows arched and his greenish eyes flicked over her. There was the faintest hint of freckling on his skin which was tan enough to save him from the sandy looks of a redhead. His hair really *was* russet, she saw now as the light fell on him. His brows and lashes were dark, another plus for one of his colouring and his mouth and nose might have been modelled by a sculptor of classical inclination.

'Sorry to frighten you darling—but I couldn't have you screaming, now could I? With your projection, you'd be heard in Tweed Heads.'

Projection? What was he talking about? Was he mad? Dru edged away as the man looked around. 'My God, I did ask Eric to find us a place off the tourist track, but I didn't think we'd have to make do with a dump like this. He must have let that brainless secretary of his make the booking.' Us? Dru wondered which way she should run to escape this crazy man. Up or down? her foot slid on to the next downward step. Down—she might make it to Sam's cottage . . .

His smile flashed out again and she was dazzled by it—the shape of that smiling mouth made her blink. Where had she seen a smile like that before? Dru pressed back into the shadow.

'I'm glad you came. It's been a long time hasn't it?' he said easily. 'Remember last time—wonderful.'

'Last time—now look——'

'Why the devil did you have to make such a fuss when you heard me coming? You were expecting me and you were obviously waiting for me——' he indicated her nightgown and Dru's mouth dropped open. 'Very flattering of course darling, but I've done a bit of travelling tonight and I'm beat. But tomorrow——' the green eyes smiled promises galore and he took a step that brought him up to Dru's cold, shivering form. His hands rested on the wall either side of her. He lowered his head and touched his mouth to her shoulder. Dru shrank from him. In comfortable familiarity he curved a hand to her breast.

'Ah, Shelley——' he sighed.

She kicked him in the shins. He was booted and it couldn't have hurt but it surprised him enough to step back.

'First of all I am not your darling,' she said coldly, 'Second, I am part-owner of this *dump* and am here on holiday.'

He stared, bent his head and peered at her in the

part-shadow. One hand went out to push back her heavy hair for a closer look but she slapped him down.

'You're not Shelley,' he said.

'No.'

'I thought there was something different about you—but in this light—there seems to be some mistake. I rented this place. Eric said——'

'Look—*who* is Eric?' she demanded, her head reeling with the idea that he might be the tenant she'd been expecting to take the other half of the house while she was here. That didn't appeal to her at all. They rented to nice, ordinary family groups who arrived at a conventional hour. She looked again at the powerful figure, the vaguely familiar face. Oh no, she couldn't have him here.

'My manager,' he said. 'He paid in advance for the flat. Or rather his secretary did. Eric would never have knowingly booked——' He glanced around then seemed to remember he was talking to the proprietor, 'Here's the key I used to get in.' The metal chain and tag clinked as he pulled it from his pocket.

'That's my spare—you should have one with a blue tag.'

He shrugged. Dru cooled somewhat. It had been a genuine mistake. At least that was a relief. It wasn't the first time the agency had supplied the key to the owner's flat instead of the one they rented out. But it was the first time it had created a mini-drama.

'Why did you manhandle me like that and why were those men looking for you?'

'I would have thought that was obvious—Miss——?'

'Winters. Dru Winters. And no, it isn't obvious. We'd better sort this out. You go downstairs and I'll put something on.'

She put on a dressing gown. When she went down he was standing in the lounge room, hands sunk in his pockets. The light was a blaze here compared with the dimness over the stairs. Dru watched him for a moment where he stood by the television set. And her brain made the association. He saw her eyes go from him to the television screen and his eyebrows went up.

'Don't tell me you didn't recognise me?'

For maybe ten seconds she stared at him, beginning to think it was a dream again. This was the Ransome Man.

'I just realised,' she said shortly, her misgivings tripling, 'the light on the landing isn't as strong or as flattering as the ones you usually work under. I suppose I should say I'm pleased to meet you, Mr Matthews.'

Locke Matthews. Screen and television actor whose international career had literally balanced on a razor's edge. It had kicked off as the result of an advertising campaign for Ransome razors and blades. In each of six different commercials, Matthews portrayed the action man in a perilous mini-adventure that had him fighting, fencing, sky-diving in hair raising escapes from danger. At the end of each, bloodied, muddied and ruggedly ragged, he would gaze into the camera, raise an eyebrow and say: 'And if you think *that* was a close shave . . .' Then a quick shave with a Ransome razor and the acid test of the smooth chin would be carried out by one or more luscious, lustful-eyed women. 'A Ransome Man is a handsome man——' one would purr rather unnecessarily as the now suave, tuxedoed Matthews sipped cognac, viewed his fine art, or idly made a brilliant chess move. The Ransome Man became one of those wild advertising successes, like the Winfield cigarette ads that long before had launched Paul Hogan. Locke Matthews had played the role ever since off screen as well as on with regard to the women, if the press could be believed. His television series, *Ramage* had run three seasons, was into re-runs and rumoured to be going into production again soon. In it Matthews did all the things that the Ransome Man had done, except that it took an hour each time instead of two minutes. In his films, the same things took over two hours. It said a lot for the economy of advertising. But his ratings were high, the *Ramage* show took out regular television awards and he was popular both on and off screen. Locke Matthews was a rare thing among the new crop of Australian stars. Still a bachelor and still choosing to live in this home country in spite of international film success. Both circumstances endeared him to press and public alike—the former relishing his many affairs and the latter forgiving him all because he was not only sexy, successful and single but he managed to subdue his ego in interview to emerge as Mr Nice Guy himself.

Had she not been so frightened, Dru might have known him sooner and apparently Mr Matthews was thinking the same thing.

'You *must* have been terrified,' he said drily.

'It's not every night that the country's number one sex symbol drops in and grabs me as if I'm a sack of potatoes,' she said sharply. 'Anyway, you look different in person.'

'So I'm told.'

'You don't look so—red-headed on the screen and the freckling doesn't show,' she told him, angered by his calm assurance as he followed her into the kitchen and sat down.

'No?' He leaned back and put the backs of his hands to his eyes, flexing his shoulders so that the sheepskin collar fell apart to reveal a chest hugging tee shirt. 'I wish more people had trouble identifying me, Dru. It would make life easier if there were a few less fans about. How about some coffee?'

He looked tired she thought, as his hand went to the back of his neck in a massaging movement. And he sounded sincere. Perhaps he wasn't as conceited as she thought. After some hesitation she put on the kettle.

'I suppose those men looking for you were Press.'

'You got it.'

'Is it still the business of the M.P.'s wife?' she asked distastefully as she put out two cups and the sugar. The stories linking him with Dorothy Falkland had been gathering strength for weeks. It served him right to be hounded. Anyone with his moral outlook should expect it. But it was a pity he'd landed on *her* doorstep. Her hand shook as she opened the jar of coffee. That shock on the stairs had pumped so much adrenalin into her system that she would be lucky to sleep tonight after all. And that raised another problem which she shelved temporarily.

He sighed. 'Damned papers.'

'How did you get here?'

'Bike.' He reached for the coffee, wrapped his hands about the cup. Bike? She should have guessed by the clothes. But what was the star of *Ramage* doing travelling by bike? Dru sat down opposite him at the scrubbed timber table. Screen actors just didn't drop in to her ordinary life—on a bike—pursued by the press. She looked down at her sensible blue dressing gown and a snort of laughter escaped her.

'Something funny about a bike?'

'No. It just occurred to me that I might be dreaming all this.'

He smiled as if he was used to women thinking his presence a beautiful dream. Which he probably was.

'Don't let it go to your head, Mr Matthews,' she said and he blinked at her tone, 'I'm not one of the swooning female fans who make life difficult for you. But as you've just scared me out of my wits in the middle of the night I might be excused for thinking I was having a nightmare.'

'You certainly *were* scared,' he said, as if she was chicken-hearted, 'You fought like the devil.'

'You think that's unusual?' Dru retorted, 'Ask any woman how she'd react if you grabbed her in the dark and see what she says.' His quirked brow made her see how crazy *that* was. Most women would react favourably to being grabbed by Locke Matthews—in the dark or anywhere at all. 'Any sensible woman,' she added.

'And is that what you are, Dru? A sensible woman?'

'Too sensible to be overwhelmed by a celluloid image, Mr Matthews.'

'What? I won't have to fight you off?'

'No. You can sleep in peace. As your—friend— hasn't turned up you probably will.'

'Are you always so direct?' he asked, annoyed.

'Mostly.'

'Then I imagine you always sleep in peace.'

Colour flushed her cheeks. 'I do.'

'With some women I'd be inclined to take that as a challenge.'

'With some women you'd be right.'

'But not you?'

'Just think of me as your landlady. Will you be staying the whole two weeks?' She waved a hand at the cosy but dilapidated surroundings. Not what he was used to.

'As a hideout it has its merits.' He drained his coffee cup and stood. 'Thanks for the coffee. Now if you give me the right key, I'll move into my flat.'

Dru took a deep breath. 'That's a problem, Mr Matthews. I don't have a spare with me at the moment. My brother took it away with him unintentionally last time he was down here.'

'You mean I can't get in?'

'Not tonight I'm afraid. However, I'm sure you'll find a suitable motel back along the highway——' she began when he raised a hand tiredly to his eyes. There was a certain eloquence to the gesture that caught at her. 'On the other hand, I do have a spare room with bunks and I suppose you could have that——' she hurried on as he trained those green eyes on her, '——just for tonight. I can get the proper key from the agent tomorrow.'

'I'd be grateful,' he said in a mellifluent voice that reached up and down her spine. She was instantly dubious about her decision.

'There's no need for gratitude, Mr Matthews. It's my fault as part-owner that the spare key wasn't here.' She walked from the kitchen to the stairs. Her shadow on the landing was overlapped by his as he followed her, picking up a leather bag on the way through.

She switched on the light of the small bedroom that was piled with odds and ends in boxes and a couple of suitcases. Double bunks stood along one wall.

'I'm afraid you'll have to share with some baggage.'

'I've shared with worse.' He dropped his Gucci bag on the floor.

'I'll bet.' She muttered and went to fetch sheets and a towel from the linen cupboard. When she returned the sheepskin collared coat lay across the lower bunk and he had stripped off his tee shirt. As she stopped in the doorway, he tossed the garment on top of the coat and came forward to take the linen from her. It might have been a scene from his show. Getting the shirt off was a must in every *Ramage* episode.

'You're young to be a landlady,' he murmured as he stood close to her, the folded sheets tucked now under one arm. 'You don't entirely fit the image.'

'I fit it perfectly well, Mr Matthews,' she said, turning away from the rather disturbing close-up of the famous Matthews torso. 'Let me show you where the bathroom is.' He followed her again, looked in as she switched on the bathroom light.

'I did a play once about a landlady. Come to think of it *she* was young.'

'There you see, Mr Matthews, I do fit the part.'

'I played the lodger . . . we saved on sheets at any rate.' He looked down at the single bed linen under his arm and leaned one bare shoulder on the wall. Dru met his tired, amused suggestive eyes.

'Good night, Mr Matthews.'

But it wasn't a good night. Dru lay awake until the early morning again and this time there was a new element in her wakefulness. Locke Matthews. A movie star! But he was only here by accident. Maybe tomorrow he would leave and seek the luxury he was used to among the Gold Coast high rises over the border. She heard him moving about in the room that was separated from hers only by the bathroom and got up to lock her door. What a laugh, she thought sourly as she padded back to bed. Securing her door against a man who could take his pick of willing partners! Locke Matthews was not likely to steal into the room of anyone as ordinary as herself in spite of his subtle pass earlier. She gave a brittle laugh that was more like a snort and pulled the bedclothes roughly around herself. Why, even Michael—himself no Adonis— didn't think she measured up. 'I know we've been going together a long time Dru darling—and believe me I feel guilty that I might have led you to think it would be permanent . . .' He certainly had led her to think just that. She had pinned her belief not on airy dreams but on a twelve-month old proposal. 'Will you marry me one day, darling?' was how he'd actually put it and she'd said yes and been content for wait for 'one day'. It didn't come. 'Over the past year I feel that I've—changed direction——' Michael's career in the Solicitor General's Department had benefited from an early promotion. He anticipated further rises and a future break away into the private sector—would have to throw himself into a more 'public life' . . . the long winded farewell had begun at that point to make sense to Dru. She would be a liability. No doubt his mother had pointed out to him that Dru's direct manner was a drawback, her lack of background a sad misfortune and, unlike her sister, she hadn't even the moderating factor of beauty. Gently, Michael had pointed out how much she would hate the life he hoped to lead.

The signs had been there for her to read. His mother had often taken pains to tell her about Michael's colleagues and their suitable wives. 'He's a lucky man,' she'd cooed about one, '—such a diplomatic wife. And pretty.' Oh yes, she should have seen then that the campaign was on for a wife for Michael. A wife who dressed up her body and her opinions in frills and lace, a wife who would give successful little dinner parties and who would, into the bargain, be photogenic. After all, who knew? Michael could even go into politics one day—and it wouldn't do for a potential top man to drag a drab first lady with him.

The hurt had pierced deeper when she'd seen Michael with an attractive brunette at the classier of the Department's two lunch haunts. Michael himself she continued to see frequently. As she worked cataloguing the statistics that Michael needed, it was unavoidable. But it was an effort to give him the no-hard-feelings smile and a flippant remark to hide her emotions. After a month of it she applied for holiday leave. It was an unfortunate time to choose. Locke Matthews would have come and gone from here without her being any the wiser if it hadn't been for Michael and his mother and his brunette.

She threw off the covers and went to the window. The broad expanse of sand looked cold in the moonlight—the glittering sea colder still. Sounds came again from his room. Apparently his weariness hadn't been enough to make him sleep. Perhaps Mr Matthews didn't care to sleep alone, she thought acidly as she got back into bed.

It was more than likely she *had* dreamed it all, Dru thought when the seagulls woke her. The early, low rays of sunlight reached her through the window that she always left uncurtained to the view. The gulls shrieked louder and she went to look. That would be Sam, tossing down the remnants of his gutted morning catch. Raising her hand to shade her eyes, Dru saw the old man, fishing rod a-quiver across his shoulder, his body listing against the weight of his fishing bag and bait bucket. He looked for all the world like some derelict old craft with more than its share of patches and an uncertain mast sprouting above. Sam had been giving the seagulls early breakfasts here for as long as she could remember. He was as taciturn now as he had been when she had crouched as a child on the sand to watch him scale and clean his catch with silver flashes of his knife. Just how old he was, she couldn't tell. Sam had always been old. And always there. Every holiday. In a way she thought, watching him tack his course through the soft, yielding sand crests to the grass verge, Sam was the only constant thing in her life.

Her parents were dead—gone before their time in one senseless, fateful twist of a car wheel. Barry, her brother was married with two children and a business to build and his life was full of new priorities. Gillian, three years older had never been really close. Her sister, with her glamour hostess job jetted in and out of Dru's life with stories of faraway places and far-out men. There was just this jointly inherited house, divided in two, as a reminder of holidays when they had been a family. And now Michael who had seemed to promise constancy, was gone.

Sam's fishing rod disappeared between the cotton-wood trees where his tiny house crouched. She stayed at the window to marvel at the daylight warmth of the sand and the sea. Sunlight made all the difference. Even late April sunlight which had lost some of its sub-tropical heat but refused to surrender to Autumn.

She heard sounds from the spare bedroom.

'Oh, hell,' she muttered and whirled into the bathroom, splashed cold water on her face, cleaned her teeth and hurried out. In the hall she marched right into her house guest as he emerged from his bedroom. Her shoulder hit his upper arm and the impact sent her staggering. He grabbed her to steady her and Dru got her first daytime close-up of Locke Matthews.

This was the sex-symbol himself. Unshaven, his squared-off, classical chin bristled reddish brown. His hair was roughed up in peaks at the crown, spiky over his eyes and he looked as if he'd tasted something bad. He was wearing only pyjama trousers and these were low slung. So low slung that at first she dared not look down lest he was wearing nothing at all. A smooth, brown chest muscled down to a smooth, brown waist. In fact the tan was even all the way to his hips where the pyjama pants clung so precariously.

'Good morning, Mr Matthews,' she said and stepped away from him. The man was so *evenly* tan. She would have to warn him not to try deepening it all over on her beach. The thought of looking out her window at him naked on the sand made her blink a few times. 'I hope you slept well?'

He ran a hand through his hair, yawned and scratched his chest. Sex-symbol! She grinned. 'If you want to lose a few troublesome fans, let them see you like this.'

He put one bare shoulder to the wall, as he'd done the night before. 'Some of them *have* seen me like this.'

Her mouth tightened. 'What a thrill for the lucky ones.'

'They seemed to think so. Have you got any coffee on?'

'I haven't even been downstairs yet, Mr Matthews,' she looked him up and down, '—but if you care to get yourself cleaned up, there'll be some ready in about ten minutes.'

'Something wrong with the way I look now?' He spread his forearms and his hands fell naturally into the relaxed fingered pose of the actor. There was a gleam in his eyes. He wanted to squeeze some admission from her that she found him irresistible she supposed. Mr Matthew's pandered ego was in for a few jolts.

'You're unshaven, unkempt and almost undressed,' she told him coldly. 'And if you want coffee or anything else, you'd better not come downstairs looking like that.'

He straightened, put his hands on his hips. 'Good lord—I could be at home again. You sound just like my mother.'

'Sorry about that. I'm sure you're accustomed to some early morning adulation over your coffee. I'd provide some but I'm just not a good enough actress.'

His greenish eyes narrowed. 'I'll settle for coffee.' As she began to walk away he added, 'I definitely won't be wanting—anything else. *Cold* breakfasts don't appeal to me.'

She didn't turn around. Her face was flushed but she admitted she had probably asked for the unflattering inference. To him she must look not only cold but also plain and prudish. He would not be even remotely interested if she *was* the type to offer more than coffee. Last night he might have been able to overlook her obvious failings. But then he'd been tired and no doubt not seeing too clearly. It was one thing,

Dru thought as she made coffee and showered cornflakes into a bowl, to know oneself to be average in every department save that of commonsense and quite another to be reminded of it so often. Bleakly she took her first sip of coffee and stared out the kitchen window at the battered old shed and its cape of convolvulus. A motor bike gleamed there in the morning sun. Michael—she thought—Michael with his ordinary, clever face, Michael whom she'd loved for nearly two years, had found her lacking. For a while she'd been angry. She hadn't cried. Not at all. The hurt and humiliation had eventually settled too deep for relief by tears or anger. This listlessness was worse, far worse than her first jealous reactions. At least when she had been able to rage about his perfidy, it had seemed some sort of positive response.

She heard Locke Matthews on the stairs and her hackles rose. The surge of anger was a welcome thing. A positive thing. She turned around, her face set in cold, hard lines. The man looked devastating. There was no denying it. Reddish hair—the faint freckling and all. He was incredibly good looking. Now his hair was combed carelessly back, his jaw tanned and smooth and he wore an open mesh sweater over shorts.

'Do I pass, Mum?' he mocked and again spread his arms.

Dru set another cup on the table. 'Your coffee, Mr Matthews.'

He sat down, not touching it and watched her eat her cornflakes. And listened too, no doubt. Dru was irritatedly aware that she was making a noise as she crunched the cereal.

'It occurs to me, Dru, that you shouldn't be handing out criticism over correct breakfast dress.' His critical eyes lingered on her disreputable tee shirt and jeans.

'I'm the landlady remember? I can come to breakfast any way I want. Besides I'm working.'

'You said you were here on holiday.'

'So I am—but as I own this place with my brother and sister, we have to maintain it, so I'm working as well.'

'Maintain it?' he mocked and looked outside to the fall-about shed. One eyebrow shot up.

'Just be thankful we don't keep it like the kind of places you're used to, Mr Matthews. Otherwise those press friends of yours would be hanging about waiting to hear what you plan to do about your latest amour.'

A vision of Michael's brunette floated into her mind just then and she wondered how long he'd been seeing her before he'd shaken off faithful Dru—whether she had been taken home for Mama's approval yet. Off with the old, on with the new. Men could do it so easily. But this one had a bit more trouble getting away with it. There was some odd satisfaction in that.

'It's garbage,' he said, 'all those stories about Dorothy Falklands and me. The woman visited the studio and I had some coffee with her.'

'Those men seemed to think there was more to it or they wouldn't tear around in the middle of the night after you.'

'It's my fault. I told them I was getting married soon.'

'According to what I read, you're always about to get married or you're already secretly married. You must be crazy telling them that if you want a peaceful holiday.'

He let his head roll back and sighed. 'Don't I know it. But it got to me I guess. The same old questions about any woman who's been seen even talking to me. The same old speculations over who is——' he stopped.

'In your bed?'

He grinned. 'So direct. You wouldn't like to marry me would you, Dru? And stop all the guesswork?'

'Is this an official proposal?' she enquired. 'Should I go weak at the knees?'

His laugh was wry. 'At least I'd know you don't want me for my body—or my alimony.'

'I don't want you for anything,' she told him. But of course others would. His looks, his money, his value as publicity for an ambitious actress. And presumably the man had his personal attractions too. He'd never really know if it was Locke Matthews being loved, or the Ransome Man. Her sympathies were almost engaged when she remembered the 'companion' he'd mistaken her for last night.

'Tch, tch. Poor Mr Matthews. Success, riches and persecution. So you arranged to drop out for a week or two. When does your friend arrive?'

'Today I suppose.'

'You don't really remember what she looks like do you?'

'I remember. But women change their hair, the light was terrible and I haven't seen Shelley for six months.'

'And she agreed to come on holiday with you after all that time?'

'Why not?' he levelled those green eyes at her. 'We're friends—consenting adults.' Aware of her disapproval, he added provocatively, 'Lovely girl, Shelley.'

'So lovely that you can mistake *me* for her! We're all the same to you, aren't we, Mr Matthews?'

He took his time looking her over. Her face flamed. What an idiot she was, inviting comparison with the kind of women he knew.

'Oh no. Not all of you.'

'Can't you manage to enjoy yourself for two weeks without——' she began and couldn't bring herself to be that direct.

'What's the matter—can't you bear to sleep alone?'
He finished his coffee and stood up.
'How did you guess?' he said mockingly and went.

CHAPTER TWO

IT wasn't sympathy for him that later made her wheel his bike inside the shed. It was commonsense. She didn't want the press snooping around spoiling her holiday. Dru collected some sandpaper from the shed and began working on the side of the house. When a car approached, she turned to watch it. Cars along this road were few, very few.

It was white and natty. A neat little hatchback with lovely lines. It turned in at the bumpy drive and stopped. The girl who got out was a neat little ash-blonde with lovely lines. She smiled at Dru.

'Hi. I'm looking for Sea Winds.'

Dru studied her. She wasn't quite what she'd imagined Shelley would be like. But if she was looking for Sea Winds, that must be who she was. The sign, like so much else, was in need of repainting and Dru had only removed it two days ago. It lay in the shed awaiting her attention.

'I thought it would be along here but there's nothing but shacks—oh, I'm sorry—I mean——' the girl glanced at the house with its peeling paint and stopped. 'Am I on the right road?'

Dru couldn't really be sure what prompted her to say no. It could have been the girl herself—so attractive, confidence in every hand gesture, the careless expertise of cosmetics and clothes. It might have been Locke Matthews' subtle digs, his casual male memory that had allowed him to mistake a brunette for a blonde—or it might have been Michael's rejection finding its way to the surface again in a misplaced hit back. But whatever it was, the girl had taken her own and the car's lovely lines and gone again within minutes. And Locke Matthews hadn't even appeared on the scene.

A whitish veil of dust marked the natty car's turn back towards the main road and Dru watched with a sudden rush of guilt. She shouldn't have done that ... she really shouldn't, and she couldn't give herself one good reason for it but spite. Dru found that uncomfortable.

The real estate agent in Coolangatta opened at eleven on Sundays. Dru was waiting at the door when the on-duty agent arrived. But also waiting was a young couple who were gazing starry-eyed at the land sale window display and he was far more interested in them than in finding a missing key. At her insistence though, he looked several times and could not find the Sea Winds tenants' key. She 'phoned Barry but there was no answer. There was no point in contacting Gillian. She was probably away, or zonked out from her latest flight and anyway her part-ownership was purely financial. Gillian wouldn't be seen dead at the holiday house and didn't possess a key. Two locksmiths offered recorded messages and Dru rammed the 'phone back on the hook and left the booth. Another night with Locke Matthews hanging about seemed unavoidable. She supposed she would have to give him dinner as well. As she crossed the Queensland border and drove back through Tweed Heads into New South Wales, Dru gritted her teeth. The very last thing she felt like doing was catering to the needs of a man—any man, but as this one had paid his rent and inadvertantly been given the run-around she would have to.

It was after twelve when she drove her car up beside the house and into the shade of the mango tree which served as her garage. The beach was empty but the row of tracks across it remained evidence of the visits of holidaymakers from the next cove. People rarely drove on to the beach here because of the unsealed road and the swampy creek beside it. Families trailed along the sand from other beaches but rarely stayed. They preferred the beach further south where the surf was patrolled by lifesavers. Sometimes couples strolled its length, arms wrapped about each other in lovers' insularity and Dru had come upon the occasional two or three girls baring their all to the sun on the privacy of the sand dunes. But they never appeared more than once. One sighting of Sam, his clothes flapping about his gaunt frame, his lips moving in private dialogue was usually enough to send them elsewhere to untie their bikini strings.

From the mango tree the lawn, rough and threadbare in the sandy soil, ran outwards to a tangle of goatsfoot creeper and the succulent ground cover that ran wild to the sand. It reappeared in clumps and questing runners on the low dunes that flattened out on to the beach itself. The surf crashed and shattered itself into foam fleck and fine spray and the horizon cut a hazed indigo line to separate the sky's slow motion from the sea's quick replays. Dru's eyes moved down from the drifting clouds to the solitary figure running along the edge of the surf.

For no real reason her anger surged up, made her hands tighten into fists. He had every right to be there—to run on the beach that she thought of as hers, but which wasn't. Just the sight of that masculine figure infuriated her. She watched for a moment the rhythm of his loping stride against the blue-green sea then went inside. If any new crop of topless sunbathers caught a glimpse of him the beach would be simply *littered* with nubile bodies stretched out to catch his eye. Sam wouldn't be enough to discourage them in that event. Dru muttered and slapped butter on two slices of bread to make herself a sandwich.

Maybe she should go back to Brisbane and leave Mr Matthews in sole occupation. When he came in he was windblown, faintly pink in the face and wearing a shirt that reached to his hips and barely touched the upper edge of swim trunks that were only just decent. His mood certainly had improved. The famous grin flashed white as he held up a large fish. The smell wafted about the kitchen.

'Dinner,' he said.

'Whose—yours or mine?'

Locke lowered the fish and closed his smile. 'Such a gracious landlady. I was going to cook it for you. As some small reparation for frightening you on the stairs last night.'

'I've made *my* lunch,' she said and picked up her uneaten sandwich.

'I didn't say lunch—I said dinner.' His mouth compressed, 'If you hadn't been so damned sour, I was going to come over tonight and make you a meal to remember.'

'Thanks but no thanks. I don't need a meal to remember.' I need one to forget, she thought as desolation found its way through her new, therapeutic anger. 'And I'm afraid you won't have to "come over" as you put it, because I still haven't got your key. There must have been a mix-up with my brother's friends who last rented the flat.'

Locke gave a sigh of exasperation. The fish flapped back and forth in his hand.

'Hell, what if Shelley arrives today?'

'There are the double bunks,' she suggested. He threw her a dark look. 'I'm sorry about the key,' she said briskly, wondering how she could explain her misdirections if Shelley *did* come back. 'If at all possible I'll get hold of it today. Otherwise—there is a Motel not far away . . . or you can use my spare room again tonight.'

He made a sound of disgust. 'This is——' he began, raising his hand in resignation. The fish swung to and fro like a pendulum.

'—a fine kettle of fish?' she finished, unable to resist it. There was something delightfully ridiculous about Mr Wonderful, locked out of his rightful rented flat, with that fish dangling at the end of a graceful actor's gesture.

He stared at her. A faint smile edged her mouth and she held out a hand to him.

'Are you trying to hypnotise me with it, Mr Matthews?' The scales glistened silver-grey-silver-grey and he looked down at the fish as if he'd forgotten its existence. 'You'd better give it to me. I'll put it in the fridge.'

'Well, well—so there's a sense of humour inside that lemon skin you wear.'

'Not all of us put everything on show,' she snapped, regretting already giving in to her sense of the absurd.

'It's a pity you don't remember that about others,' he returned cryptically. 'Here, catch.'

The fish landed in her arms and she gave an involuntary cry of aversion as the cold scales touched her skin. In a flurry of movements she juggled it, holding it by thumbs and forefingers to slap it on a plate. And all the time he laughed—a low chuckle that grew into a belly laugh at her grimaces. At last she put the plate on the refrigerator shelf and slammed the door shut on it.

'Very funny.' She washed her hands and turned to look at him. He was in his favourite pose—one shoulder against the wall. Why on earth was the man always nearly naked?

'Where did you get it? The fish.'

'From Sam.'

'You've spoken to Sam?' She was surprised. Sam was loath to talk to anyone except herself and Barry and his family. Sometimes even she didn't see him for days at a time. Sam was a loner. 'Did you tell him who you were?'

'But of course. I went right up to him and said: My good man, I'm a film star, you'll have heard of me—how about a fish?'

'Sorry. I forgot you're not *seeking* publicity right now, are you?'

He pushed himself away from the wall, came and stood near her. 'You're pushing me, Dru. Landlady or not, if I keep getting cracks like that I'm likely to lose my cool.'

'Don't issue me with warnings, Mr Matthews. I say what I want to say and I don't care if you *are* the hottest screen property around and every fool woman's dream.'

She didn't see his hands move. They simply shot out and closed around her upper arms and hauled her to him in one smooth blur of motion. He was furious. The green eyes were narrowed, hard as malachite and she felt a flutter of nerves. If he was angry at this, what would he be like if he found out she'd sent Shelley away?

'You're not only righteous but rude. I've a good mind to——' His eyes dropped to her mouth and she felt a charge of electricity run the length of her back.

'Oh come now, Mr Matthews, that's been done to death. When the heroine gets a bit above herself she's punished with a kiss! I saw you do it in a *Ramage* episode that I was unfortunate enough to catch.'

'No, I won't kiss you. It might not prove a punishment. Not to you, anyway,' he added and his face relaxed into satisfaction at her quick swallow. Silently she flayed herself for walking into the trap so that he could tell her again what she already knew. Kissing her would be no pleasure. She had no sex appeal. 'Some have it—some don't' Gillian had said once or twice. She'd said it flippantly herself a hundred times but it always came out a fraction mistful when you knew you were on the minus end.

'Let me go please.' She pulled against his hold.

'What's the matter, Dru,' he put his hand to her ribs, just below and to the side of her breast so that his thumb touched the full underswell, 'I'm not disturbing your prudish senses am I——?'

The beat of her heart quickened at the so nearly intimate touch. He bent his handsome head and looked deeply into her eyes. Mr Wonderful was setting her up for another slap in the face.

'Let me go.'

'What's the hurry?' His arm slipped all the way about her waist and now she was against that panel of warm, tanned skin left uncovered by his open shirt. 'Am I really that awful?'

Dru decided against an undignified struggle. There were other ways of dealing with Mr Matthews and his ego.

'Not—*that* awful,' she said.

'Am I so unattractive to you?' His voice had dropped to a whisper and his breath sighed past her ear. Boy, she thought—a lot of women would give their eye-teeth to play a scene like this.

'No—o——'

'Well then——?'

'Mr Matthews,' she said softly, as he angled his head in another pretence at kissing her, '—you smell.'

He froze, whether at her criticism or her failure to be captivated she couldn't tell.

'Cut,' she said drily and removed herself from his grasp. 'A great scene, Mr Matthews, played with feeling. But you smell of fish.'

He went off to shower after that, casting a speculative look at her. Before he came back she finished her lunch, left a sandwich for him and went outside to resume her work on the much neglected windowframes. Her sandpaper rasped and the paint flakes flew as she scrubbed. Long before he spoke, she knew Locke Matthews was standing somewhere near, watching her.

'Thanks for putting my bike away.'

'Don't mention it. I didn't want your reporter friends spotting it and intruding on *my* holiday.' She stopped for a few seconds and brushed the white paint particles from the sill. 'How come you're travelling by bike anyway?'

'I like to ride occasionally. And it's less conspicuous. Though those reporters last night cottoned on. I flew from Sydney and borrowed the bike from a mate of mine in Brisbane.'

'A mate?'

'Yes—a mate. In the circus I live in there are one or two real people.'

That sounded sad. He's an actor she reminded herself. If he wants sympathy he can get it. Her fingers ached from being flattened to the sandpaper. When she paused the top joints locked and she flexed her hand.

'You're going about that the wrong way?' Locke said.

'Oh, really?'

'If you find yourself a small block of wood and wrap the sandpaper around it, you'll find it a lot easier.'

'Did you do a play about a housepainter too?'

'I did play Hitler once,' he admitted with a snap in his voice, 'But I picked up that trick painting houses for a living.'

She laughed. 'Please, Mr Matthews—I may not be sophisticated but I'm not gullible.'

'You don't believe me? I painted houses with a friend—the same one who loaned me the bike—for a year. My life wasn't always strewn with willing women and contracts.'

Dru stopped, met his eyes. She felt vaguely ashamed but just looking at him made outright apology impossible.

'How big a piece of wood?' she asked and he demonstrated with precise movements of his hands. In the shed she selected one of Barry's timber offcuts left over from a repair job. Then she did as he suggested and had to admit that gripping the block would be a great deal more comfortable.

'Thanks for the tip,' she said when she returned to her work to find him stretched out on the sparse lawn.

'My pleasure.' he murmured and checked his watch again before looking down the road. Wondering where Shelley was no doubt, Dru thought and her conscience twinged. The girl might have given up by now and booked in somewhere for a solitary holiday.

After a while he got up and went over to fiddle with the door of the flat he'd rented. Bending he peered in through the small window, rubbing the knuckles of one hand into the palm of the other.

'Thinking of breaking in, Mr Matthews? You could always charge at it and force it open with your shoulder the way you do in your movies. But remember this one isn't made of balsa.'

'If you run out of sandpaper, Dru—just use your tongue.'

She had to admit he knew a good exit line when he had one. He strode away, skirted around the mango tree and went along the beach in the direction of Sam's cottage. Whether he found a brace of topless sunbathers on the dunes or whether he found Sam himself, he didn't reappear.

Dru made another fruitless trip to the nearest 'phone box to 'phone Barry, but there was no answer. In any case, it was too late to get the key for tonight but she had been hoping to find some way to fetch it first thing in the morning. Now she would have to repeat the procedure all over again and probably make the long drive to Brisbane to get Mr Matthews' key. Either that or bear the expense of bringing in a locksmith.

'Well?' he demanded when he returned up around six and found her in the lounge.

'If you mean the key—sorry. No luck. And if you mean Shelley—again no luck,' she added at his arrogant appearance.

Why did just looking at him rile her so? Dru had an uncomfortable feeling that she was shooting barbs at Locke Matthews which rightly belonged elsewhere. But she had so many unused barbs and he had made himself the perfect target with his traumatic arrival and his calm assumption that she was there for his benefit. Until of course, he'd had a proper look at her. He was from another world. A man not quite real. It seemed not only permissible to fire at him—it was irresistible. She turned away to the kitchen.

'What time do you want dinner?'

'Good lord, are you offering to cook it?'

'In view of the fact that we've messed up your booking I feel it's the very least I can do.'

'And you intend to do the very least, of course,' he grinned.

'Of course.'

'Can you cook?'

'No. I'm terrible.'

'That's it then. I'm not handing over my fish to a terrible cook. I'll make the dinner.'

'Don't tell me—you played a chef in a play once.'

He opened the fridge, took out the fish, weighed it up in one hand and weighed her up visually.

'Nope. Got a knife, Dru?'

'How come Sam hadn't already cleaned it?' She

picked out a sharp cook's knife from the drawer and held it out to him.

'I didn't ask him.' The knife changed hands and he put the fish on a board. With a wicked, threatening glance he held the knife up and ran a cautious thumb under the fine blade edge.

'I played a murderer once ...' he purred in a Vincent Price voice.

'Did you get caught?'

'Yes.'

'Well there you are, Mr Matthews—you're better off playing the lodger.'

Her fine, fast reply left her tongue before she saw the implications. The lodger had saved on sheets with the landlady. Locke grinned, ran the knife point along the spine of the fish.

'That's what I'm doing. Again.'

'Never mind, you'll be able to ditch the role for another more familiar if Shelley turns up.'

Green eyes sparked at her. 'One thing we won't need with this fish.'

'What?'

'Lemon.'

Dru wandered about, sat in the lounge for a time and turned on the television. But it didn't hold her and she switched it off, standing there for a moment as the sound of Locke's voice reached her. He was singing—absently in an unremarkable but pleasant voice and she couldn't help thinking again how incredible it was. One—that she should have a man singing in the kitchen at all—and two, that it should be him.

'Is there anything I can do?' she enquired.

'Not a thing. Go and make yourself beautiful.'

'I meant something possible,' she retorted and as she left caught his quick glance at her.

Beautiful, she thought ten minutes later—regarding

herself through the steam in the bathroom. Fat chance. Fate had given the prime bits to Gillian—the leftovers to her. Gillian had the heartshaped face, the crushed strawberry lips, the wide, slanted eyes and model's nose. Dru had the same heartshaped face and there the resemblance ended. Her mouth was too wide, its curves flattened out more, her eyes were average, thick lashes which was a small bonus, her nose was rounded, girlish without the chiselled tip that gave Gillian's such class. Dru grabbed a towel and wiped a clearing in the misted mirror. Even in the matter of colour she had got the leftovers. For Gillian there had been china-blue, blonde and pale gold. For her there was grey, mouse and tan.

She dried off and dressed in jeans and shirt. At least her figure was okay if a bit on the athletic side. But her hair! It hung in ghastly tight curls to her shoulders. Dru towelled it, dragged a comb through its astrakhan pile then put on some lipstick and left the bathroom before the mirror cleared entirely.

The dinner was delicious. The fresh fish tasted of herbs she hadn't known were in the cupboard, the salad had a light dressing that defied identification and there was wine on the table. He had found the cupboard under the stairs then.

'This is very good, Mr Matthews.'

'Call me Locke.'

'I don't think so.'

'Worried you might get too familiar with the lodger, Dru?'

'No. I'm not worried about *that*, Mr Matthews.'

'What is it with you? Is it just me you hate—or men in general?'

'Nothing so simple. It's just movie stars I can't relate to. Why only last week I was saying the same thing to Mel Gibson——'

He laughed. 'How old are you?'

'Twenty-three.'

'Are you involved with someone, Dru? Engaged?'

'I've no intention of discussing my love life with the lodger.'

He reached out and patted her hand, poured more wine into her glass. 'Very wise. That was how it all started.'

'All what?'

'In the play I told you about. I was the lodger and the landlady started confiding her troubles to me and before she knew it we were . . .' he gave a Gallic shrug.

'Saving on sheets. I know, you told me last night.'

'Talking of last night—how come you were so demented?' he enquired. 'I mean just before I put the light on you were raving about monsters.'

Her colour went sky high. 'You frightened me.'

'But *monsters*?' he chided. 'What did you think I was—the bogey man? Not afraid of the dark are you Dru?'

'Not any more. But this was our family holiday place before my parents died and I used to be terrified of that place on the stairs—when I was about eight years old—and last night when I heard a noise I was half asleep——'

'So when I touched you in the dark . . .' He grinned and put on his Vincent Price voice again, 'I let loose the monsters of your youth.'

'There's no need to be smug about it—I daresay you have your fears, Mr Matthews,' she paused, 'Though I don't suppose being alone in the dark is one of them.'

He reached for the bottle of wine and topped up his glass. 'If those reporters find me,' he said slowly, 'I'll sic you on to them. You'd eat them alive.'

It was going to be another night of no sleep. Dru accepted the fact around midnight and didn't bother with her charade of closing her eyes and lying in the position most likely to succeed. Instead she stared up at the ceiling and tried to make a list of all the work she could do on the house. The windowsills . . . 'if you run out of sandpaper, use your tongue.' Was she becoming a vinegary old maid at twenty-three? The front doors could do with stripping down, the shed needed a new pane of glass in one window. 'In the circus I live in there are one or two real people . . .' Such a lonely sound that had.

She got up and went to her window, looked out on the cold beach. The moon shone down and made the earthly scene its own with its hills and craters, the ocean a glittering alumina sheet behind a line of foam. The surf's hollow roar merely accented the stillness of the night. No wind, no movement in the cottonwoods by Sam's place. So quiet. So still.

When it came the cry ripped through the night. Terror held Dru fast as that one note of pain, her mind blanked out to a primitive level, adrenalin pumping into her system.

The sound stopped.

She let out her breath and turned back to the silent moonscape. There seemed to be a connection somehow. Perhaps if she kept looking out at the silver stillness, that cry would not come again . . . but the sound that came seconds later was so anguished that she shot to the door and out into the hall to put the light on.

'Oh God—no——' the cry came again and she stood helplessly outside the spare room.

'Not Eva—it isn't her——' he cried and she pushed the door open. The hall light showed him to her. He was sitting in the lower bunk, looking straight ahead, eyes staring the white faintly pink. 'Only ten minutes late—she must be somewhere else, that's it——' he gabbled. Then, 'No!' He put up a hand to ward off whatever knowledge was thrusting itself upon him in his sleep. Dru went to stand beside the bunk.

Although his eyes were open, he was asleep and his body was trembling. Hesitantly she put a hand to his shoulder. The skin was ice cold, damp.

'It's all right,' she whispered, uncertain as to whether she should wake him. 'Everything's all right Locke.'

'Eva—never wears pink. Oh no. I'm late. She'll be in the shop——'

He stopped, reached up a hand to where she barely touched him.

'It's just a dream,' she said, frowning down at his shaking shoulders. 'Can't you bear to sleep alone?' she'd said. Whatever was turning him into a terrified child had chilled her too. He muttered then lay back in the bunk, pulled her so that she sat abruptly on the edge, her hand clasped in his against his chest.

'Eva——' his voice broke and she felt the distressed rise and fall of his breathing beneath her hand. His other arm curved to her waist as he turned and she found herself clutched against him. She resisted but the arms holding her were seeking comfort, nothing else and after maybe thirty secoinds of indecision, compassion won and she lifted her legs on to the bed and lay with him, her arms around his cold, beautiful body. And her sharp tongue murmured soothing, meaningless words.

CHAPTER THREE

IT was maybe five minutes before his shivering stopped. When he lay still at last in her arms, his mutterings patchy and incoherent, Dru stayed there and saw his face relax in dreamless sleep. His lips were slightly parted, his hair spiked over his eyes. What light there was from the hall lingered on the photogenic cheekbones and the arrow-straight nose. Shadow lay dark across his jaw and the hollows of his eyes. She swallowed, confused at the emotion that chased around inside her. After all she had said to him—after all her dislike she had rushed to comfort him. He groaned and she lifted a hand immediately to his forehead. At her touch his head turned to the side and he was quiet. Like a child reassured by his mother's hand.

That was what this odd, choking feeling was, Dru thought. A latent maternalism. She had seen the strong man reduced to a child and it had brought out the mother in her. Carefully she took her hand from his head. It was a powerful feeling—to be needed like this. The first time she could remember being needed. Slowly, slowly—watching him, she withdrew. Oh Lord, if he woke now and found her here . . . her heart thumped so hard and fast that she felt sure its drumbeat must wake him. But his hands slipped away from her to lie gracefully on the sheet and she stepped out on to the floor. Once more she looked at him then went with gathering speed to her own room.

Sam's seagulls mewed and complained and Dru woke. With an arm over her eyes to shield them from the morning sun, she re-ran last night's dream sequence. She had stretched out alongside Locke Matthews in his bed—had held him and felt his arms clutching her close. As she delayed the intrusion of the new day, she admitted what she couldn't last night. Her maternal instincts had been shot through with something else—the feel of him in her arms had pleased more than the buried mother in her. He had smelled of toothpaste and soap and he hadn't been wearing a stitch, not even the low-slung pyjama pants ... Abruptly she lowered her arm and let the bright light of day flood in. Her meandering thoughts shrivelled away from the light, just the way her imaginary creatures used to years ago. Dru got up and went to the window to watch Sam as usual. She just had to remember to turn the light on, that was all.

As she dressed Dru asked herself two questions. How come, for the first time since Michael's tactful jettison of her, she had stayed awake nearly all night and scarcely thought of him? And who was Eva?

'Good morning,' Locke Matthews said cheerfully when he came down for breakfast. 'You left the hall light on you know,' he went on.

'Oh.' She gulped cornflakes. In her hurry to shut herself back into her room last night she must have forgotten it. In her haste to avoid him this morning, she hadn't noticed. 'I must have left it on when I got up last night to—er, go to the bathroom.'

'And my door was ajar this morning—I could have sworn I closed it last night.'

She raised her head and the sight of him hit at her. There was a mocking smile about his mouth as he stood, one hand on his hip, the other resting on the back of a chair. He had shaved this morning. Last night that smooth jaw had been scratchy against her cheek, beneath her hand ... 'Well of course, I couldn't resist coming in to peek at my captive movie star, Mr Matthews. I'm *just* the type to moon over a sleeping sex symbol.'

He chuckled. 'You're terrible for my ego, Dru.'

'Your ego can stand a bit of a battering.'

'Maybe—but please, not total annihilation.' He boiled the kettle and made himself some instant coffee, humming as he did it.

'You're very cheerful this morning,' she remarked as he sat down. 'Did you—sleep well?' Watching him closely she could see no reaction at all. He didn't remember a thing about last night.

'Yes I did. The best night's sleep I've had for a while.'

'You say that as if it's something unusual.'

Over his coffee, he met her eyes, looked away. 'Sometimes when I'm under stress I have trouble sleeping.'

She said nothing. It was suddenly so much more difficult faced with a man who had cried out in the night. Far easier to deal with the star—the man who was an image and not a real person.

'What—no prudish cracks about what might keep me awake?'

'If you insist—it's bound to be——' she started to say 'a woman' and remembered that it *was* a woman who had disturbed his sleep last night and maybe other nights. A woman called Eva. '—too much coffee.'

His brows went up. 'Pulling your punches, Dru? You disappoint me.'

'Life is full of disappointments,' she said, 'If you like you can pack up your things this morning. I'll definitely get you into your own flat by lunch time.'

'So eager to be rid of me,' he murmured, watching her quick flurries about the kitchen.

'It makes me nervous having a star hanging around. I never know whether to curtsey or applaud.'

Dru's second, unhopeful visit to the agent uncovered the key that had been left unidentified in a drawer. She picked up some supplies for her tenant and drove back along the coast with a feeling of satisfaction that was oddly mixed with depression. After he had moved next door she ate some lunch and walked over the sand to see Sam. His cottage had grown to look like Sam himself over the years. Or maybe it was the other way around. The timber house was narrow, paint-patched and though it was sturdy enough, gave the illusion of a faint lean. The cottonwood trees clustered around it supportively, leaving only the very front of the cottage exposed.

Sam was sitting on his steps, using a small knife on a piece of driftwood. Several other beautiful twists of sea-washed timber lay in the sun. He looked up at her, his eyes squinting against the glare, the skin around them creased into a mosaic of irregular tiles of weathered, brown skin separated by pale, deep grouting.

'Aaagh,' he grunted and she smiled, sat down beside him in silence. It was his usual greeting and she had never been able to decide just what word it represented. But his nod and the smile in his eyes were enough. There was something very peaceful about sitting with him. The world and everyone in it needed thousands of words. Except Sam. His knife flashed in quicksilver movements on the driftwood. Tiny shavings and chips fell about his bare feet. She watched the knife tip follow the weather-scored grain of the timber, open it out delicately in a long, waving groove. There seemed a strange kinship in what he was doing, with the gulls' noise and the sea surge.

'What will this one be, Sam?' He turned out his small gems—worked with instinctive restraint on nature's formless art to give it form—and sold them to a local crafts shop.

'Dragon.'

After another few minutes, he stood the piece on the lower step. The back arched from the body of the branch, the water-smoothed protuberances gave support as legs—the head was a fearsome distortion, the truncated fork of the branch.

Yet it was a likeness undefined. A beautiful, natural shape in one swift glance—a creature of fantasy in the next. That was why his work sold.

'It's beautiful.'

'Aaagh.' He shot her a look from under thick, peppery brows. 'That feller—said his name was Smith.'

'Oh yes,' she smiled. Smith. How unimaginative. 'Mr Smith. You gave him a fish.'

'I like him.'

And that was that. Sam liked—Sam disliked. His summing up was usually quick and permanent. And justified—mostly.

'Why?'

'Genuine. No flim-flam about him. Knows a bit about fishing too.'

He would. He'd probably played a fisherman in something. Genuine? Perhaps Sam was a bit off-beam there. How genuine could an actor be? A seagull screamed and she thought of that painful cry last night. That was one thing at least that had been genuine.

'Sounds like a lonely man to me,' Sam said and she stared. Lonely? Locke Matthews—surrounded by managers and women and adoring fans. Who even had a companion lined up for his holiday.

'That's crazy coming from you, Sam. No-one lives a lonelier life.' To her knowledge he had lived, worked and slept alone for the last fifteen years and maybe even before that. Sam picked up the driftwood dragon and shaved a sliver from the head.

'No,' he shook his head. 'I live alone. There's a difference. It's only lonely if you haven't chosen to be that way.'

'Philosophy, Sam?' she grinned.

He chuckled. 'Don't start throwing your big words at me,' he said. 'He wanted to know about you.'

'What?' Her pulse tripped. 'What did you tell him?'

'Nothing much. Said you'd been an inquisitive brat—a dreaming teenager before you got to be so darned grown up and sensible.' He shot her another glance. 'Said you'd been almost as much trouble as a daughter to me.'

'Sam—you didn't warn him off?' A warm vexation filled her. Sam was looking out for her and didn't realise how unnecessary it was.

'Good looking feller.'

'What's that got to do with anything?'

'Used to having his own way I reckon.'

'I thought you liked him?'

'Do. Doesn't change facts. Watch your step, Silla.' The name from childhood days swept over her in a wash of regret and desolation that had some vague connection with the present. Drusilla had been abbreviated to Silla when she was young, became Dru at her insistence when she turned fourteen. Because she felt ordinary and drab and thought Dru sounded sophisticated. Only Sam kept the old name.

'Have to call you Silla,' Sam had said, 'It's pretty like you——' And when she'd protested he'd shushed her and told her to listen to the wind in the cottonwoods. 'See,' he said, 'You can hear it in the breeze.' And she even thought she did hear the leaves whispering the old name—Silla. But she didn't change her mind. And nor did Sam. Silla it always was. Perhaps that was why he seemed her only unchanged link with childhood.

'Don't worry, Sam. I'm in no danger from Mr Smith,' she said drily.

'Sounds like some regret there.'

'Of course not,' she exclaimed, stung.

'Aaagh. Just be careful,' he repeated with a shrewd look at her. When she got up to go he nodded again and his farewell was the same as his greeting.

'Aaagh,' Sam said.

Locke came over the next morning just as she finished her breakfast. There was stubble on his chin again like that first morning, and he was wearing shorts and nothing else at all. His chest was smooth, bronze and hairless and irrelevantly she wondered if he would be such a pin-up if it sprouted reddish hair.

'Finished your cornflakes?' he asked with a grin.

'What makes you think I had any?'

'I heard you——' he mocked the sound effects of her crunching cereal.

'Very funny, Mr Matthews.'

'Actually my hearing isn't that good,' he admitted and leaned over to pick a cornflake off her tee shirt, his fingers brushing the upper slopes of her breast. Stoically she kept her face very straight—very commonsense.

'Did you want something, Mr Matthews?'

His eyes remained on her breasts. Dru wished she'd worn a bra. 'Yes, I did want something. You've distracted me—oh yes, I'd like a pair——' he paused, eyes wicked and teasing and she refused to rise to his baiting, '—of pillowslips. Last night I only found sheets and blankets and some rather raw pillows.'

She stepped aside, let him in. 'This isn't the Sheraton, Mr Matthews, as even the brainless secretary must have guessed when she rented the place. But you should have had pillowslips. I'll get you some.'

He was bored, Dru thought, eyeing the alert gleam in

his eyes—and ready to make her the butt of his enjoyment. She looked mockingly at his bare chest which seemed extraordinarily prominent—as if he was sucking in his breath to impress her. But she turned away and he followed her upstairs. At the linen cupboard she turned to look at him. 'You can breathe out now. I'm duly impressed.'

'Damn me,' he grumbled, 'I'm a sex-symbol after all, or so they tell me and I can't even get my landlady to sigh over me.'

'I'm not the sighing type,' she handed him two pillow cases. 'Do you shave?'

He felt his chin. 'Going to rap me over the knuckles about that again, landlady?'

'No. I meant—there.' She pointed to his chest and he looked down, astonished.

'Shave? My *chest*?'

She shrugged. 'Well I thought you might. I mean if it grew red hair it wouldn't fit the image would it? You'd have to keep your shirt on in *Ramage*.'

He blinked. 'Shave my *chest*?'

'Hasn't anyone asked you that before?'

'Never.' He shook his head. 'Shave my *chest*?' he muttered again as they went through to the kitchen.

'Have you got everything now, Mr Matthews? Linen, cutlery, crockery?'

'Well, the crockery is a bit crude.'

'Oh dear. *Sorry*. I'll run over with the Royal Doulton later. We have this trouble with our clientele you see. They keep knocking off the china.'

He laughed. 'No-one will knock off your current lot. It's the worst stuff I've come across.'

'Look—it's plain and cheap I know, but otherwise I'm not aware that it's so terrible.'

'Come and see for yourself. Over breakfast I counted seven chips and that was just on one coffee mug.'

She went with him, trying to ignore his shirtless, unshaven glamour. Walking behind him, looking at the muscular back made her think of how he'd felt in her arms. All that strength had been of little use to him with his dreams of Eva hurting him. It was a stupid thing to dwell upon. And probably one of the reasons she made her mistake.

She was shocked when she saw that the equipment was indeed in a disgusting state. Barry couldn't have checked it last time he was down and the agency which cleaned out after each tenant certainly hadn't reported its state.

'You're right, Mr Matthews,' she said briskly. 'It's lousy. I'll get you something better right away.'

'Thank you, Miss Winters,' he half bowed. 'How about making my bed for me while you're here?'

'This is a flat not a serviced apartment.'

He went to the kitchen counter and picked up the receipt he'd shown her that first night. 'It says "service included",' he said with malicious pleasure.

'But it can't——' she looked at it. He was right and the amount paid did appear to cover some extra facility.

'But we *never* provide service to the flat——' she protested and her temper began to rise at the look on his face, '—we don't have any arrangements for someone to come in.'

'I don't want someone to come in,' he told her. 'In no time at all my presence would be all over the coast. I want you.'

She reddened, annoyed at her reaction to the phrase. 'I won't do your housework for you, Mr Matthews. Just because your curvy little ash-blonde hasn't shown up, don't imagine that I'm going to . . .' Her words slowed. Her colour heightened.

'Curvy—little—ash-blonde?' he repeated.

'Well——' she stammered, 'I imagine your friend

will be curvy and more than likely blonde. Isn't that the type you go for?'

She backed away at the look on his face. Her guilt was showing and she couldn't control it. What a fool—she might have simply bluffed it out if she hadn't blushed and backed off. His hand clamped about her arm just below the elbow.

'You've seen her, haven't you?'

'Let me go—you're hurting——'

He had her fast now, using both hands to hold her squarely in front of him. With her palms against his bare chest she pushed but nothing happened.

'Why, you little bitch—you've seen Shelley and didn't tell me. Did she leave me a message?'

'Don't you call me names,' she shouted, as much from fright than anything. The man was powerful, far more than she would have imagined and though she'd made him angry before it was nothing compared to this. 'Yes, I saw your girlfriend whose face you can't even remember. She was really quite attractive—she'll be furious if she ever finds out you mistook *me* for her!'

The hold on her arms loosened and Dru whipped her shoulders one at a time from his grasp.

'Did she ask for me?' he enquired, very clearly, very controlled. Dru backed a step.

'No. She wanted to know if she was on the right road to Sea Winds and the sign wasn't up and I——' she couldn't finish. She was in the wrong, there was no arguing that. Her conscience stung. From her own inner resentment and hurt had come one moment of spite that still amazed her. Whatever the man's morals, she had had no right.

'And you told her she wasn't?' he finished for her, in that same quiet, dangerous tone. 'Why *was* that, Miss Winters? Sat in judgement have you and decided that I'm not to be allowed any joy on this holiday?

Does that mean, prudish little mind of yours want to deny anyone else the pleasure you deny yourself? Or can't get because of your sourness?' he gritted the words between his teeth.

'No—I don't know why I——' she began apologising but as he came towards her she stepped back in a hurry, bumped into a kitchen chair so that it thumped to the ground. Then she turned and ran through the small lounge to the front door. She flung it open but discovered that all that running he did on television was genuine, not speeded up. He caught up with her as she opened her own flat door, took her arm in a tremendous grip and half led, half carried her inside. 'Mr Matthews——' she shouted, wanting to make her apology and end all this. 'Locke——' But he marched along, not leaving room for her so that she stumbled behind him, bumping the wall and a sharp table corner before he whirled her into the sitting room with one yank of his arm. Before she could catch breath, he sat down on the divan taking her with him in an undignified sprawl across his knees.

'What are you doing?' she screeched up at him. The green eyes were malachite again, the sculptured mouth marble hard. He rolled her over and held her down with one hand manacled about her neck while the other—the other smacked her backside with a force that shocked the breath from her. The pain near her hip, where she had bumped the table, diminished at the burning humiliation he administered. It stung her body and her pride. The tears that should have fallen for Michael's rejection, fell now. Self pity brimmed up with this sharp, searing punishment. He hoisted her to a sitting position and looked impassively at her wet face. Dru staggered to her feet. The tears having started at last, would not stop. They rushed in hot, blinding gushes and streamed down her face. She ran from the room, went the wrong way in her distress, turned about and found the stairs. The suppressed sobs made whooping sounds in her throat and when she reached her room she fell on the bed and curled herself into a defensive ball and let the crying out.

At his first touch on her shoulder, she burrowed further into the bed. Firmly he moved her until he could see her face. He looked contrite. And surprised. The sobs wouldn't stop as he put his arms around her and eased her on to his knee. They didn't stop for long minutes as she sat there like a child in a father's arms.

'Dru——' he murmured. 'I'm sorry. I over-reacted. But you shouldn't have done it.'

'I—know——' she managed in a jerky voice and then somehow bits of it spilled out—Michael and his mother and his brunette and lost dreams and love and the loneliness of being a misfit—'I was so miserable and so angry at everything that when you came along I let fly with it all. And it seemed all right to be rotten to you . . . you weren't like a real man.' She looked up at his frown. 'I mean—you were make-believe *Ramage* and the Ransome Man—not a real, hurting man.'

He gave a short, dry laugh. 'I see. A dummy you could stick pins into?'

'I suppose so. I'm sorry. Because I know——' you are a real, hurting man, she began to say, thinking of the night she'd held him. '—I know I offended you.'

He reached for a box of tissues on her bedside table and mopped up her face.

'You've been a little bitch that's for sure and I've been a class one brute, so I guess we're even. Are you normally sweet and gentle then?' He grinned as if he knew the answer.

She shook her head. 'No. It's my sharp tongue and my—well I can't abide schmaltz if you know what I mean. Too direct, that's my trouble.'

'Well I'm no angel either. But I'm not a brute, not off-screen.'

Dru pulled away from the delicious comfort of his arms. How could the touch of the man who'd so humiliated her be so—so satisfying? She stiffened and slid off his knee on to the bed so that she was sitting beside him.

'Shall we declare a truce?' he asked looking sideways at her.

'I suppose so,' she replied jerkily, 'but once I've replaced your grotty utensils we won't have to see each other anyway. Well hardly at all.'

'No, no. You'll be in every day to clean up and make my bed for me——'

The bed bounced as she swivelled to face him. 'I told you—I'm no domestic servant.'

'. . . and,' he went on as if she hadn't said a thing, 'I think it's only fair that you stand in for Shelley considering the way you sent her packing.'

She sat stock still, wondering if she was hearing right. 'Stand in? Why you arrogant, lecherous devil——' she jumped to her feet but he grabbed her and toppled her backwards. She hit the mattress and the bedsprings bounced and squeaked frantically before slowing to a steady rhythm. Locke bent over her, holding her wrists to the bed.

'Just go easy with the lecherous accusations, Miss Prude. It's true that Shelley and I had something going a while back . . .'

'Oh you've actually remembered a few of the details have you? Her face, even?'

'God, you're a shrew aren't you? I should have given you a few more whacks while I was at it. This Michael must be on his knees giving thanks for deliverence from you.' The hurt pierced through her and she paled for a moment.

'Then you won't be wanting me, will you? Just run

along the beach and show off your muscles for ten minutes or so and I'm sure you'll get any number of offers——'

'You'll fill in for Shelley. You caused the problem and you can fix it,' he said with a tough set to his mouth. The bed squeaked again as Dru tossed around to escape him, but he held her.

'I won't. You can manage without—without sex for a couple of weeks surely.'

'Good God,' he said scathingly, looking down at her tumbled mouse hair and tear-blotched face. 'You don't think I want you for that? My dear girl, Shelley and I would have enjoyed a holiday together but she was also intending to help me learn my lines for a play.'

'A play?' She was still, face a furious red from his amused dismissal of her as a sex object. The liberationists went on about it, she thought—men making women their playthings. But some of us just aren't in danger. He let her go and got up.

'Shelley's an actress?' That must have been what he meant about projection when he'd stopped her screaming that night.

'That's right. But you'll have to do.'

'No. Sorry. I just wouldn't be any good at reading lines.'

'You'll manage. We'll devote each morning to it. Right after you've washed up, made my bed and cleaned the flat. And I'd like clean sheets every day.'

'Yes my lord,' she touched an imaginary forelock, 'If you leave out your boots I'll lick them for you, your handsomeness.'

Unexpectedly he laughed. 'Look, Dru, I'll make a deal with you. I want my flat serviced—okay? And I need someone to feed me lines—you do that with me each morning and I'll help you with the house painting for a couple of hours each afternoon.'

'But you're on holiday!' she burst out, surprised at the offer when he'd shown every sign of making her a slave of her conscience.

'Painting is a relaxation compared to my work. Is it a deal?'

'What if Shelley turns up again?'

'In that case the deal is off.'

She might come back. Please let her come back, Dru intoned silently. Then she would not have to get any more involved with this man than the odd 'good-morning'. Her hip was hurting where she'd run into the table, her behind smarted from his slaps and her pride stung from his sarcasm. A holiday she had thought, in the one place that stayed the same, to help herself adjust to a suddenly aimless future.

She gazed at Locke Matthews' half naked figure and the carved beauty of his face. Sighing, she looked out the window at the lonely beach and the sky's blue dazzle. A gull swooped down over the house and low over the sand dunes. Its single scream floated back to her—a lonely, hurting sound. 'All right,' she said. 'It's a deal.'

CHAPTER FOUR

THEIR bargain was to commence in an hour. Dru cleared away her own breakfast things, put on her bikini and a towelling jacket and walked across the dunes to Sam's house. It was closed up and though she walked right around it there was no sign of Sam. His bicycle was gone. Perhaps he had gone to deliver another tissue wrapped consignment of driftwood sculptures to the gift shop.

Dru looked back at the little cottage with its dilapidated timber fence almost on the sand itself. How old was it? And how old was Sam? She frowned. Too old surely to be riding his bicycle on roads like theirs, even if he was wiry and strong. She dropped her jacket to the sand and raced into the surf, pushing away the unwelcome thought that even her long friendship with Sam could not last forever.

The sea was cold. She plunged under a wave and surfaced again, to swim along parallel to the beach, enjoying the sensation as she settled into her crawl rhythm. Then turning over, she cut smoothly to a racing backstroke, feeling the swell and fall of the sea beneath her. By the time she let a surge carry her to the shallows, she was tingling all over, and she ran from the sea smiling, tossing back her head to wring the water from her hair.

Locke Matthews was stretched out on the sand near her jacket, wearing next to nothing again, she observed. He had a disreputable cloth hat pulled down over his eyes, hiding the famous face. But if any of their nubile sunworshippers happened along, that wouldn't disguise him for long.

'Where did you learn to swim like that?'

'My father taught me.' She reached for her jacket, using it to dry herself. 'He was Olympic class once—a silver and three bronze medals.'

'Not Wes Winters? Good grief.' His eyes wandered over her figure. 'He taught you style.'

'Thanks.'

'Why don't you wear your hair like that more often?'

'What? Soaking wet?'

'No—I meant, pushed back from your face. I've just realised that until now I haven't really seen you— you've been shrouded in all those curls.'

She slipped on the jacket, said drily: 'You haven't missed much, Mr Matthews. And speaking of faces—if you don't want to be recognised I'd advise you to wear some dark glasses as well as the hat.'

He looked up at her, squinting in the sunlight and managing to look sexy even so. 'I'll bear that in mind.'

'Well, don't say I didn't warn you. The dunes attract a few little dolly birds now and then to bare their all to the sun so they can go back south with an end of season tan. If they were Locke Matthews fans they'd probably recognise you without even getting a look at you face.'

He wasn't amused. Perhaps he didn't always like being a mere sex symbol.

'Well,' he said sourly, 'I suppose I could always stop shaving my chest. That might confuse them.'

The first script reading of MAN ALIVE was not an enormous success. Dru was self-conscious—aware that she would be miserably inadequate in the most amateur of company.

'Can't you try to differentiate between the lines a bit . . . .?' he asked impatiently when she had read the parts of Rhoda 'glamorous divorcee', Beresford 'a charming effeminate' and Henry Smallwood 'humour-less academic' in exactly the same tone.

'Look, I'm no actress,' she glared at him. 'And I can't even begin to approximate a glamourous divorcee let alone sweet Beresford and stuffy Henry.'

'Give me a slight change of tone—anything,' he sighed, 'So that I know who's giving me my cue.'

She tried. But it was alien to her and embarrassing. 'It's all such tripe,' she said as they abandoned it two hours later.

'It's certainly tripe when you read it,' he came back, 'It's a good comedy.'

'Why are you doing a play at all? Surely films and T.V. are more lucrative.'

He grunted. 'I just needed to get back on a stage to remind myself what real acting was like—even if it is only a lightweight role.'

Real acting? She looked at him curiously. 'What did you do until you became the Ransome Man?'

'I didn't *become* the Ransome Man,' he said irritably, 'I just filmed a few commercials for a razor company.'

'Well I remember them and you certainly seemed to become the Ransome Man. You've been playing him ever since haven't you?' He was silent, slapping his script against his thigh. 'I mean, *Ramage*——' she went on, '—surely that name similarity was no mistake and the character in that is basically the Ransome Man with a bit more time for fighting and bedroom scenes. And I've only seen one of your films but it didn't seem much different from Ransome—except of course that you didn't shave in it.' She grinned at him, 'Come to think of it, for a man who built his career on selling razors, you don't use one all that often do you?'

He made a bow. The script crackled in his hand. 'Thank you, ma'am, for such a generous summing up. You make it sound not quite respectable, but I can assure you thousands of actors would give their souls to get where I am today, even if my career is—as you so succinctly put it—based on selling shaving gear.'

Who was he trying to convince, Dru wondered. It was coming through loud and clear that he was frustrated. She'd already had a hint that he found the sex-symbol label limiting.

'If you had the time over again, would *you*?'

'Would I what?' he glared at her.

'Give your soul to get where you are?'

He threw the script down. 'Oh for God's sake, don't be so damned melodramatic.'

It seemed more than likely, Dru thought as she went back to her place for lunch, that Locke Matthews found his superb looks something of a liability at times. She peered at herself in the mirror, dragged back her hair with both hands and studied the result. There seemed no improvement to her in spite of his expert opinion to the contrary. Her hair fell back in its thick crinkles around her face as she washed her hands. There were more important things in life than appearances. Even film stars seemed sometimes to think so.

True to his word he helped her with her painting, though that too, was not entirely successful. His previous experience made him think that he could take over the entire operation.

'This paint is terrible. How long have you had it?'

'No idea. It was in the shed.'

'It's like painting with oatmeal porridge.'

She bit back her reply to that but when he began criticising the sequence of her work she rounded on him.

'If this is how you intend to help I'd rather do without. Either that or I'll write *you* a script.'

'With me cast as a "yes" man?' he smiled.

'That's the general idea.'

'You wouldn't like that at all,' he told her. 'A man who didn't do battle with you would bore you in minutes.'

'Tch, tch Mr Matthews. Don't generalise. What I like in an assistant painter is not what I necessarily like in all men.'

'Was Michael a "yes" man?'

'No. He wasn't.'

'Did you fight with him?'

'Not a lot.'

'Call him names. Disagree—make him lose his temper and spank you?'

'No.' She painted furiously. A fine spray of white flew from her brush as she batted it back and forth against the tin's edge to get rid of the excess.

'Sounds boring.'

Slap, slap, the brush went along the frame. Boring? She'd never found it boring. Well, maybe some of those quiet Sundays spent with his mother at their beautiful old Ascot house. It was an odd thing about that house. Gracious, lovingly tended, full of fascinating furniture and classy paintings and ornaments, it had no warmth. No welcome. They would have atmosphere in *their* home, Dru had always promised herself. Michael agreed with that. 'Of course—it's important to have the right feel about a place, to make guests relaxed.' That wasn't what she'd meant. Her idea was a cosy retreat for them both and one day their children. Michael had been planning cocktail parties to further his career and he hadn't pictured her as the hostess. Boring? She had to admit her attention wandered a bit from some of Michael's club after-dinner speakers. And he hadn't always approved of her bald comments. Her irreverent attitude was a sign of immaturity he'd told her once . . . or twice. Often.

'What's the matter, Dru?' Locke asked, watching her explosive painting style. 'Do you still love him?'

'Silly isn't it?' she said. 'We aren't all as well adjusted as you, Mr Matthews! Of with the old, on with the new. It takes me a bit longer than five minutes to stop loving someone.'

They finished the work in silence. Dru continued for a time after he'd gone then cleaned out the brushes, removed the speckle of white from her arms and face and went to see if Sam was back.

His door was still shut and she felt vaguely worried by that. She sat on his steps, idly picking at the long grass growing up through the treads, and watched the ocean. Sam's cottontrees were throwing mottled shade across the dunes before he came home. The rattle of his bicycle sent her around the back to find him wheeling it under cover of the ramshackle shelter. Dru stopped in surprise. He was wearing a suit! An ancient one, quaintly wide lapelled and very square in the shoulders but a suit nevertheless. It was very loose on him. He had some old fashioned bicycle clips around his lower calves, holding the fabric close.

'Sam—I didn't know you *owned* a suit!' she exclaimed and he swung around looking startled. Just for a moment he seemed displeased at her presence, then he smiled.

'Aaaagh. Coming in, Silla?'

She followed him inside. His house had entranced her as a child. Everything in it was either hand made or made over by Sam. And everywhere were the mementos of his long association with this beach. The tongue and groove walls were hung with treasures—a segment of a rusted marine engine, a crab pot, shells, the huge, sea-smoothed splinter of crate timber with faint stencilled markings, a ragged fish net. Worthless things. Everything in the place was worthless she supposed in money terms, except perhaps the chronometer and sextant both polished and loved as reminders of Sam's father to whom they had once belonged. Then there were the driftwood pieces in varying stages of evolution into a fantasy menagerie. Atmosphere she thought, smiling. Michael and dear, refined Mrs Pennington just didn't have a clue about it.

'Where have you been, Sam?' He had removed his jacket and started on the tie that was knotted tightly at his neck.

'Here, let me——' She loosened the knot and Sam slipped off the necktie with a sigh of relief, then undid his top shirt button. He was wearing braces. There was something very vulnerable about his thin, wiry body in the baggy suit pants hoisted unfashionably high by navy and red striped braces. These clothes could have been in storage since the war. Dru felt uneasy for some reason.

'Had a few things to tidy up in town,' he said and filled his battered kettle with water.

'In Tweed or Coolangatta?'

His peppery brows were drawn down. The tiles of skin over his cheekbones were clearly marked. 'Nope. Brisbane.'

'Why didn't you say? I could have driven you.'

'Got the bus from the Heads.'

'Sam, I don't want to pry but what on earth was important enough to get you into a suit?'

He lit the tiny gas stove, bending down to adjust the blue flame. 'Had to meet my brother,' he said at last.

'I didn't know you had one.'

'Neither did he,' he gave a dry chuckle. 'Thought I'd kicked the bucket years ago.' He glanced at her, put the kettle on to boil. 'Never got on with him you know. Didn't get on with him today. Didn't think I would, but I wanted to see him one—one of these days, so—I did.'

Sam made the tea in a dented, scratched silver

teapot. He'd found it on the beach years ago. Dru remembered him showing it to her and Barry and they'd spend an hour or so inventing stories to account for anyone leaving a silver teapot on the beach.

'I know who he is, Silla.'

'Who?'

'This fellow Smith. Saw a poster in town. Locke Matthews.' He shook his head. 'Found a lot of things on this beach. Never a film star.'

She laughed. 'Does he rank with the teapot?'

'Don't know yet. Everything all right?' He looked at her with the eyes of a father. Anxious, protective. Caring. 'Of course, but——' She explained about Shelley. The old man fixed her with thoughtful eyes. 'He was upset that I'd sent his girlfriend packing but to compensate I'm filling in for her—helping him learn his script.'

'Is that what he said she was coming here for?' he grunted. Her laughter rang out. 'No. She was going to be his bedmate as well. I'm only filling in for her in the daytime.'

'Hmm. Sounds like you're putting that Michael out of your mind.'

Sam didn't like Michael. Whereas he had decided on one meeting that he liked Locke, he had come to the opposite conclusion with Michael. It was true that Michael's first comment about Sam's place had been about the value of the real estate and he had been a few seconds too late in wiping away his disdain at the tiny cottage. Sam had not been appeased by his tactful cover up. He had been pleased when they broke up.

'Silla,' he said after one of his long silences, 'Do you see much of Barry and Gilly?'

She told him, shrugging that they were engrossed in their own lives. Gillian away much of the time and sleeping off jet-lag or dating when she was in town. Barry, building up his construction business and fighting to find the time to spend with his wife and kids, let alone anyone else.

'You need someone. Someone who needs you,' Sam said, almost to himself. Trust Sam to say it in the least number of words. Dru picked up the driftwood dragon from its shelf and admired it.

'Haven't finished it,' Sam said.

'No. It's not quite a dragon yet.' She set it down. A beautiful shape in the blink of an eye, a hint of the creature in the next. 'It could be almost anything you wanted it to be,' she murmured.

Sam's tough skinned fingers took it from her and he looked piercingly at her. 'What would you like it to be?'

'I don't know.'

'Let me know if you find out,' he said. 'I'll do what I can.'

Dru watched hopefully for a natty white hatchback, but Shelley had given up it seemed. At nine the next morning she knocked at her tenant's door. He answered it wearing only the low slung pyjama pants and stubble.

'Don't you *ever* dress?'

He looked sleepily surprised. 'I'm on holiday.'

'Well, why didn't you go to a nudist camp—then you could leave everything off.' She walked past him with a disapproving look at the near indecent pyjamas. 'You might as well.'

'In *that* case——' he grinned and untied the cord of his pants.

Dru's mouth dropped open. She spun around and went with all speed to the kitchen. He disappeared while she did the chores. His clean sheets went on, depleting her spares to one pair. She bundled up the used ones to take home to wash.

'Will you have enough bed linen for a daily change?' he asked when he saw her with them.

'No, of course not. We don't keep fourteen pairs of sheets, Mr Matthews. I don't know anyone who does.'

'Have you got a washing machine?'

She widened her eyes at him. 'Good lord, I'm not going to WASH them! Sheets that have swaddled the body beautiful! I thought I'd tear them up into little squares and auction them off. Then I could afford to *buy* fourteen pairs of sheets.'

She left him laughing.

The play reading was more fun this time. She was less self conscious. It was the glamorous divorcee Rhonda, that defeated her.

'Look, I know you're not an actress, Dru, but do you have to sound so wooden?' Locke asked when he'd repeatedly got Guy Latimer's cues wrong. 'In those few passages her lines are rather similar and I'm relying on her change of mood to bring me in with the right response.'

'Your friend Shelley could no doubt say all those things about being a beautiful woman with sincerity, but I feel a fraud.'

'If you hadn't stuck your nose in Shelley *would* be saying them, wouldn't she?' He studied her face. 'Anyway, beautiful is as much a state of mind as anything.'

'Huh!' she snorted. 'Easy for you to say.'

'Dru—do you think only beautiful women ever get the beautiful parts?'

'Don't they?'

'Not always. *Actresses* get them. And they *act* beautiful. Who is the best looking woman you know?'

'Gillian,' she said without hesitation. 'My sister.'

His eyes narrowed a bit at that as he came over to her. 'How does she walk—as if she *knows* she's good to look at. I'll bet she doesn't hunch her shoulders——' he put a hand to her back and pushed her erect, '——or hold her head like a turtle afraid to leave its shell unless it comes out snapping.' He adjusted her head, tipped her chin up. 'How does she talk? As if she *knows* people want to be with her. In short, she *acts* beautiful. Actresses don't wait to get the perfect face and figure, Dru—they adopt all the other things that go with them. And anyone can do that.'

'Even me?' she squeaked, holding with some exaggeration the posture he'd forced on her.

'Okay—you want to be plain. Go right ahead. But you've got a choice.' He went back to perch on an armchair. 'Just try putting a little oomph into those lines will you, so that I can tell one from the other.'

Want to be plain? He was probably right. With Gillian around it had always been useless to compete in the beauty stakes. Barry had the brains, Gillian had the beauty and Dru—well, Dru was *such* a character. People had always said so. She had found her identity in a kind of anti-beauty flippancy. All wisecracks and wild hair. *Such* a character, Dru. Glamorous divorcee Rhonda came out, if anything, rather less vibrant and Locke closed his script with a sigh.

'Sorry, Mr Matthews,' she said. 'Is there any way we can get in touch with Shelley?'

He stared at her as if he'd forgotten the girl again.

'What? Oh, I shouldn't think so. And call me Locke.'

'Is it real—the name?' Rather ironic, she thought—a man called Locke with the wrong key.

'First my chest, now this,' he grumbled. 'Yes, it's real. Derived from my given name Lachlan. My mother would be very happy to confirm that.'

'I'll take your word for it. I won't be speaking to your mother will I?'

'I wish you could—she'd like you.' He smiled, gave it some surprised thought, 'In fact with your dislike for schmaltz she'd like you very much——'

She began to move to the door, reluctant to dwell on the idea of being liked by Locke's mother.

'All right. "Locke" it is. We're painting the side windows near the shed today.'

He saluted. 'Yes ma'am.'

'First we have to sand them down and do the patching.'

'Yes, ma'am.'

'Start at two?'

'Yes, *ma'am*.'

She laughed. 'You're shaping up nicely as an assistant painter.'

Later she ruefully admitted that he was more useful to her than she was to him as Shelley's stand in. He was already applying undercoat to his window and she hadn't finished sanding hers.

'It's only natural,' he agreed goadingly. 'I've been around, tried most things. Experience.'

'That must account for your overweening confidence.' she muttered.

'Confidence! I'm glad you think so.'

Curiously she studied him. 'You *are* confident, aren't you?'

'How would you ever be certain,' he mocked. 'I'm supposed to be an actor remember.'

Supposed to be.

'You never did tell me what work you did before you became—made those razor ads.'

He acknowledged her tact with a smile. 'You don't want to hear all about the bad old days—my starving days——' he pulled his mouth down, 'when I did all the audition rounds, worked as a drinks waiter, came up north to do some theatre and ended up painting houses instead, sold spray painters door to door . . .' He sighed, let his shoulders droop.

'My heart bleeds for you. I'll bet you had a great time.'

'Oh sure. Front up for an audition, wait for three hours only to have the part cast before you even get to try out. And if you were lucky, you'd actually get to show what you could do—after two lines someone down in the dark in G row would shout up, "That'll do. Leave your name." Of if you were really impressive a producer might stop you and tell you how close you were to getting the part. "But you're a bit too young, son," or "Too pretty, my dear, but *do* leave your number anyway——" He glanced at Dru and obviously censored the rest of that one. "I almost got a part today," you could tell your friends over a hamburger and then rush off to work in the pub.'

'Did you ever study acting?'

He gave a snort of laughter. 'The lady needs to ask. Yes, I graduated from NIDA. I'm still friends with a couple of my class. A lot of us started out with ideals—but the fact is, you have to live and you can starve on ideals. From Pinter and O'Neill and Williamson you soon snatch at walk-ons in soapies and radio voice-overs and—commercials.'

'And that was your lucky break—getting the Ransome ads?'

'It was Eric's baby—that campaign. He was working for an advertising agency and dreamed up the Ransome Man idea. He suggested I audition for it and I did—fair and square. But there were those who claimed I got the job because I was family.'

'Family?'

'Eric is my brother,' he explained. 'As well as my manager and agent. Thank God. In a business like mine, it's a rarity to have someone you can trust absolutely.'

'So your brother gave up advertising to manage you?'

'That's right. He saw the potential when the Ransome thing took off and promoted me for a year before anything more happened.'

'He sounds like a good friend as well as a brother.'

'He is. He got me through a very bad patch just before the Ransome thing came up and another long before that when our father died.' He stood back, looked contemplatively at his work. 'I owe him. Without Eric I could even still be painting houses.' He held up his paintbrush and grinned. She laughed, thinking that he couldn't owe his brother that much careerwise. After all, Locke's break into the big time wouldn't have done Eric any harm. From advertising agency to management of a superstar. That was almost as good a success story as Locke's own.

'Did you do much television work before Ransome?' It was hard to imagine that he had gone unnoticed.

'A soapie bit part—and I did a play.' He laughed to himself. 'I was twenty-two and nervous as a kitten I remember. It was the first time I had to do a screen love scene.'

'You—nervous about a love scene?'

'Think it's easy do you?' He slanted her a wry look. 'I'd done a couple as a student on stage but there they last only seconds and the audience get a long view. The cameras pick up every little detail in close up and I was worried that I might look peculiar——'

'Peculiar?' She stared.

'It's a personal thing—kissing someone,' he shrugged.

'I mean while you're doing it, it seems okay, but you never *see* yourself doing it, so you don't know if you do it like everyone else—or if you look ridiculous——' He looked over at her. 'These things weigh heavily on your mind at twenty-two.'

Dru threw back her head and laughed. 'You can't be serious.'

'I am,' he declared. 'That play had me chewing my nails. And the lady—the kissee you might say—didn't help. She thought it was funny. Kept fouling up the rehearsal so that we had to do it over and over again.'

She probably fancied him, Dru thought.

'How did she foul up a love scene?'

'Just by turning her head——' He put down his paintbrush and wiped his hands on his shorts. Then he came over and took her shoulders, shuffling her around to face him. 'I had to sweep her into my arms——' He did so and she felt the sudden thump of her heart. She clutched her sandpaper against his bare shoulder. 'I would tilt my head like this.' Dru swallowed. His handsome face came into sharp focus, the green eyes teasing, '—and just as I got close enough to kiss her, she would tip her head in the same direction so that our noses clashed.' His hands went to her head, turned it to demonstrate. Their noses rubbed together. For maybe five seconds they stayed like that. Dru dragged her eyes from that beautiful mouth and stepped back. There was some new, crackling awareness in the air that jolted her heart beat into thunderous speed. Dru heard the sea and the gulls and the whisper dry movement of the breeze in the mango tree.

'But you discovered that you were just great at love scenes,' she said lightly.

'I discovered that it's mostly camera angles.' He took his paintbrush up again and told her about the only film he made as an unknown. 'Gruelling location work. Bush flies and heat and tents for all but the leads. The tent I had blew away in a duststorm and I chased it on a bike to get it back.' He laughed as if the memory wasn't entirely unpleasant for all the flies and dust. 'At the time I thought that film would be the spring-board to better things. But the commercials came along right after that, so . . . I sometimes wonder where I would have gone without Ransome . . .' He glanced at her and grimaced. 'Or if I would have gone anywhere at all.'

When he finished his window he went away and she

saw him treading over the dunes to Sam's place. She laughed. Locke Matthews, uncertain that his kissing style was orthodox! Dru dipped her brush in the oatmeal-thick paint. She had wanted for those few brief seconds to be kissed by him. There was no denying it. Had he felt the need for a real live love scene she would have been willing. The brush moved rapidly along the thirsting timber. But he hadn't felt the need.

The next day fell into a similar pattern. Dru gave glamorous Rhonda a little of Gillian's style and if she felt silly doing it at first, had only to think of Locke, nervous about his first screen kiss, to recover.

In the afternoon they painted the lower front windows. Locke whistled while he worked and occasionally sang. His russet hair was spiked and tipped with white paint. No shirt, scruffy shorts, bare feet. He was relaxed and good natured. If it wasn't for his amazing looks he could be any nice, ordinary man doing a spot of painting. It didn't seem possible that he was a superstar, accustomed to luxury and the fawning attentions of men and women alike. Dru smiled as he burst into song again. He looked over and grinned.

'I know—I know—I've never played Caruso.'

'Of course not. You're too young,' she said with a sly glance, '—and too pretty, my dear——'

Locke dipped his paintbrush in the tin and wiped it off purposefully. As he came towards her Dru giggled and backed off. 'No, don't you dare——' But he caught her against the wall and dabbed paint on her nose. He leaned his arms on the wall each side of her and watched her scrub the paint across her cheek. 'Okay, I suppose I deserved that,' she admitted when he took a rag and cleaned her up. 'I should be kinder to you. It's not everyone who would help me with the painting after what I did.'

'I'm glad you appreciate that. Will you reward me?'
'How?'

'Give me that kiss I almost took yesterday.'

Her heart bounced around in teengae fashion. 'Oh-oh, you must be getting bored again, Locke.'

The look in his eyes was hard to define. Amused, but something else too. 'No,' he said softly, 'I haven't been bored for a minute since I came here.'

Sam came over later to catch them laughing over one of Locke's film anecdotes about another 'unnamed' celebrity.

'What do you think, Sam?' Dru indicated the lower floor of the house, still as dilapidated as ever but for its gleaming windowframes.

'Flash,' Sam said with his usual economy. He chewed his lip while he inspected their work. 'You'll have the place looking so good there'll be film stars and such like clamouring to stay here.'

Locke threw a speaking look at Sea Winds. '*Clamouring* you think?'

'Not what you're used too. A dump, I hear you called it.'

'I've grown to like it, Sam. Quite a lot.'

Sam narrowed his eyes then gave a funny little nod.

'Aaagh. Caught a mess of fish this morning. Want to barbecue them on the beach tonight?'

Dru was enthusiastic.

'Allow me to bring the wine,' Locke said. 'If I can borrow your car to go to the pub,' he added to Dru.

'Aren't you afraid you'll be mobbed by adoring fans?'

He looked expressively at Sam. 'Dru will bring the lemon.'

The moon was up when she walked out on to the sands. Over near the cottonwoods the fire was already lit—its flames a warm flare of colour in the indigo night. She could see two figures tending it. Sam crouched, his long, thin limbs making almost a stick figure of him in silhouette. Locke stood beside him, leaning forward in a listening attitude. She heard the faint sound of their voices, then laughter. For a moment she stopped on the dunes, took a deep breath of crisp, salty air and looked up at the star scattered sky. It seemed a night to sing or shout or dance. Dru felt happiness bubble up inside her as she ran across the cool sands to the fire.

'I've brought some plates and glasses,' she said breathlessly, putting down her basket. Both men looked up at her, seemed arrested by what they saw. She had a scarf tied around her head, holding back her mass of hair, wore jeans that frayed at the edges, and a sweater. Her feet were bare. 'What's the matter?' she directed the question at Sam.

'Nothing that I can see,' Sam said.

The fish were wrapped in foil, suspended over the fire by a grate. A faint, delicious smell wafted from them occasionally to mingle with the tang of wood-smoke and sea-salt. Locke expertly uncorked the wine, poured it with a flourish.

'Your stint as a drinks waiter?' Dru raised her brows at him.

'Just so, ma'am.' There was a glint in Locke's eyes as he brought her the glass. His face was dramatically lit by the fire, the sculptured nose throwing a dark shadow, the beautiful mouth curved and generous. It was two days since he had shaved.

'I see that look in your eye. You're going to reprimand me for not shaving aren't you?' he said.

'It would be nice. But I suppose at least you're dressed tonight. One out of two isn't bad.'

Locke chuckled. Sam's head popped up like a bird alert for trouble.

'I'm growing a beard as a disguise. So I won't be attacked by my devotees when we go shopping tomorrow.'

'We?'

'You and Sam and me,' he grinned. 'We thought we might help you with the shopping seeing as you've invited us to dinner tomorrow night.'

'Oh, did I? And did I tell you just what I'd be cooking for you?'

'Don't believe you did. Did Dru mention the menu, Sam?'

'Close as a clam about it, she was.'

'Well, if you're game, I am,' she said cheerfully. 'You both know I'm a lousy cook.'

The fire's embers glowed scarlet. The fish were pronounced ready.

'Sam, this is delicious. It tastes like being a kid again. Remember when——' It was the first of a dozen 'remember when's'. Locke heard about her maddest escapades with Barry and Gillian, heard about the silver teapot and of the cereal packet plastic coin Dru discovered and took to Sam, babbling of Spanish doublons.

'I was only about ten.'

'And a dreamer,' Sam smiled gently at her across the fire, '—always thinking to find treasure on a junkheap, always the one to see visions in the fire. The one to take risks.'

'I grew up, Sam,' she said drily, a little embarrassed at this unusually flowery speech from him.

'Aaagh. Pity.'

He fell silent after that, content to watch them and the fire and listen to Locke's stories, taking for granted the names of cities he would never see, the names of the famous who were nothing to him. The two men had some odd affinity that defied their vastly different backgrounds. Only days ago Dru had found Sam's approval of Locke irritating. Now she was warmed by it. Glad for the old man whose taciturn nature admitted so few. Glad for Locke too.

It seemed natural that they should sing as the fire glowed down to its last embers. Under the stars with the moon swinging slowly over in her arc, they sang the songs that Dru remembered from other childhood campfires on this beach. Locke was only stuck for words once. His voice joined robustly with Sam's wavering tenor and her own reedy sound. Binding them.

Sam became introspective again when they fell silent, then said goodnight.

'Sleep well, Silla. Locke will see you home.' It was a command. She smiled and waited obediently by the dying fire while Locke followed Sam inside with his barbecue tools and rug. She heard their voices, low from the house as a window showed light. It seemed a long time before Locke came back. The fire had gone out and she stood up and stamped her feet in sudden chill. Then he was there, gathering up the basket with the plates and the glasses. He kicked some sand almost angrily over the dead ash of the fire, and took her arm.

The sea shushed and shattered. The shadows were mauve-grey on the sand as they followed the marks of their footsteps that curved around the beach to the dunes. Locke's arm slipped about her shoulders and he pulled her close against his side. Dru knew this was the moment for some light-hearted witticism but her throat was dry and no words would come. On the dunes near Sea Winds, Locke muttered something under his breath and dropped the basket to the ground with a rattle of china and glass. He spun Dru around to face him, looked down at her while the moon moved a little on its arc and the sea rushed once, and again to the shore.

Then he kissed her and the earth itself was moving

beneath her feet. His lips were tender and Dru felt a pang of longing. He drew her close against him, his hands searched the width and length of her back. Her mouth parted. What was tender and sweet became sensuous . . . and she was lost. Moonlight and indigo closed in. She held Locke tight in her arms and new, painful knowledge burst into her consciousness. Their breath mingled as they drew apart and looked at each other. Locke smiled at her and there seemed to be compassion and tenderness in it. Compassion? She stared into his eyes and saw it was true. Pity was there.

Abruptly she stepped back. She was so angry that she could have hit him—so angry that tears were stacking up behind her eyes and tightening her throat. So the ordinary girl-next-door had been given a thrill had she? A real life love scene in the moonlight featuring Mr Wonderful himself.

Dru picked up the basket and the plates clunked.

'You might have shaved first,' she said.

CHAPTER FIVE

IN the morning they went shopping in lieu of the usual line rehearsal.

'It doesn't matter,' Locke said about the lost time. 'Rehearsals don't begin until the end of July. I'm being very conscientious starting on my lines so soon.'

They bought the groceries, packed the refrigerated goods in the portable icebox and had lunch at a pub, sitting under an umbrella in a courtyard of tubbed palms and banana trees. No one recognised Locke. They lazed and laughed their way through meat pie and three veg and drove home again in the same closeness that they had achieved last night. It was Locke, Dru thought as she drove. He was sprawled in the back seat looking out the window and she watched his mirror image with a dry feeling in her throat. He had stumbled into Sam's life and hers and in an odd way, bound them together with him. Even with the memory of that charity kiss, she couldn't resent it. The closeness that she and Sam had always shared was enhanced, magnified by Locke's presence. And whatever faults he had, she wanted it to go on. Another week. That was all there was. Dru watched the road turn from macadam to rutted dirt as she took their turnoff. It would be a week to remember and after that? She bit her lip. Just—a week to remember.

Correction, Dru thought as they reached Sea Winds. Today was the beginning of remembering. A natty, white hatchback was parked in the road. Shelley had come back.

'Your friend is here,' Dru said brightly to a drowsing Locke. He sat upright and saw the car. 'Now don't forget, her name is Shelley and you had a simply *wonderful* time when you were last together.'

He took off his sunglasses and sent her a withering look.

'See you later, Sam.' He touched the old man's arm briefly and got out. Shelley appeared from the seaward side of the house and waved gaily to Locke. Her gleaming lips moved in greeting and she reached up and kissed his cheek, winding her arms about his neck. Locke put his arm around her waist and took the blonde inside with unseemly speed.

'Well,' Dru said briskly, 'That's the last we'll see of him today by the look of it.'

Sam narrowed his pale eyes at her as she got out of the car and slammed the door.

'Aaagh.' He looked closely again as he helped her take the groceries inside. The fridge door flung shut a few times as she emptied the portable cooler. 'Silla,' he stilled her jerky movements with a touch to her arm. 'Come over and have a cup of tea with me.'

'You like him,' he said as he poured from the silver teapot.

'Don't you?'

'Aaagh. That's different.'

'We had a lot of fun last night,' she said, trying to keep it general, 'And today. Just the three of us.'

Sam had been working on a new piece of driftwood. It was the head of a unicorn. The wavy cracks in the wood looked like a curly mane. She picked up the dragon that was still unfinished. Sam had worked a little more on it, so smoothly that the mark of his knife was not visible. It could be, even now, just a piece of driftwood.

'Decided how you'd like it to be yet, Silla?' the old man asked, watching her.

'No,' she said and looked from the window over towards Sea Winds.

'Thought you might have,' he said drily. Dru looked sharply at him and put the dragon down.

'Leave it as it is, Sam. Neither one thing or another.'

'I'll keep it for you. Put your name on it, Silla . . .'

When she walked across the dunes, Locke was waiting for her, arms folded across his chest. The white hatchback was gone.

'What are we painting this afternoon, ma'am?'

'Where's Shelley?'

'She was a bit put out when I showed her the inside of the place—didn't fancy staying here.'

Dru looked sceptically at him. 'Even with you as a bonus?'

He shrugged, turned his mouth dolefully down. There was a sting of salt in the air. The sky had clouded over and a breeze lifted sand into powdery flurries. Dru tried to crush the rise of her spirits.

'Did you tell her there were clean sheets every day?'

'She wasn't impressed.'

'You could have gone up to one of the high rise resorts with her.'

'I could. But what the hell, I can have luxury anytime. It's refreshing to live shabby for a change. Besides,' he grinned at her indignant face, 'I have a dinner date tonight.'

Her face was pink. Locke wanted to stay here with them. He had alternatives and chose to dismiss them. Suddenly she felt like singing again.

There were several dinner dates for the three of them that next week and another beach barbecue outside Sam's place. Dru woke every morning with an eagerness she hadn't experienced for years and slept dreamlessly each night. Only one night did she wake and then she paced around in helpless frustration as she heard Locke cry out twice then stop. In all his humourous tales of location work and Hollywood parties, she never heard mention of Eva or any event

that could give him nightmares. Not once again in that
week did he kiss her or even put his arm around her.
But he reached out to her in a hundred ways with
words and smiling eyes—as a friend, though she knew
by the end of their time she was taking his friendship
and wishing it more than that.

Locke's beard was a disreputable, bristling growth
by the time he had to leave. They had a party the
night before. Sam played his harmonica and its
nostalgic strains gave all their songs an air of *Auld
Lang Syne*. But he was coming back Locke said.

'In November—I'll get Eric to arrange it——' he
grinned, 'Or rather, Eric's dopey secretary who made
such a lucky mistake with my booking——'

'Told you,' Sam grunted to Dru. 'Paint the place
and film stars start clamouring to stay here.'

She didn't believe a word of it. Locke Matthews
would never come back here. Would never have come
here but for a mistake. If she wanted to see him again
it would be in the row of a movie theatre or in front of
a television set.

'I'll get in extra sheets,' she said.

Sam was with her when Locke wheeled the bike
from the shed in the early morning. There had been
some rain during the night. The sand was pitted with
the drops, the mango tree was still shaking down small
flurries of rain with the breeze. It was the first week in
May and the air was crisper.

The two men shook hands, holding the clasp
strongly. 'Remember what I said,' Sam grunted.
Locke nodded.

'Remember what?' Dru looked from one to the
other.

'Man talk,' Sam told her.

'I'll remember.' Locke was casual. Came over to
Dru and took her by the shoulders for a quick peck on
the cheek. His beard scratched at her skin but he

straightened away all too soon. She didn't even have time to touch him.

'Good luck with the play,' she said lightly.

'Thanks,' he smiled at her. He raised a hand in unsmiling salute to Sam, held it a moment. 'Goodbye, Sam.'

'Bye son.' The words were lost in the roar of the bike. Locke put his helmet on and looked at them through the shaded visor. Then he was gone. A trail of dust rose behind him. When it dispersed on the breeze, Sam took her back to his house and gave her tea from his beachcomber's teapot.

'I hate goodbyes,' she said to explain her watering eyes. Sam took her hand and held it tightly.

'So do I Silla,' he said. 'So do I.'

She had another day of her holiday left and woke to the sound of the gulls bickering over Sam's fish trimmings. At the window she saw him listing across the sand with his fishing rod a-tremble and the shadow of the gulls flickering hopefully over him.

When she locked up the house that afternoon and packed her car, there were a couple of Sam's morning catch in her icebox.

'I'd like to see you happy Silla,' he said, when everything was done.

'I am, Sam. This has been a marvellous holiday.'

'Things change,' Sam said cryptically. 'You had to grow up some time. Getting rid of that Michael was good. You're too old for a security blanket.'

'Security blanket—Sam!'

'That's all he was to you, Silla—with your parents gone and your family tied up, you wanted guarantees for the future. Aren't any. If you go for what you want there's no guarantee at all—but don't ever settle for second best.' He gruffed, 'I love you girl.'

She had always known that. Even when her parents were alive, Sam had been there for her. It was rare for him to tell her though. He could sense her need right now. She hugged him. 'And I love you, Sam McGinley. I'll come down soon for the weekend and we'll sing your songs again.'

'Aaagh.' said Sam.

But there would be no more songs for Sam.

She had been back at work a month, restless and unable to concentrate. Her nights were restless too. She had exchanged one kind of loss for another. And the third loss . . . the third was a quiet, educated voice on the phone.

'My name is Desmond McGilney, Miss Winters.'

'McGinley?' she repeated. 'Sam's brother?' A kind of chill set in, starting at her feet.

'He left instructions with me, Miss Winters. Asked me to call you to let you know when . . .'

The funeral was simple. The sun shone and a few gulls flew over the cemetery which was near the coast. Sam would like that, Dru thought. There were just six of them apart from the minister. Barry and his wife Jan, Gillian, Desmond McGinley and his wife. Dru couldn't cry. It didn't seem real to her. Sam was still in her mind as she'd last seen him, waving goodbye to her as she drove away.

'I love you girl'—that and a dozen other things should have given her the clue. But how easy it had been to ignore clues to something she preferred not to face.

The minister's voice was a fuzzed background noise. There were footsteps on the gravel path behind them and she felt the others turn their heads. After a moment she looked around. Her eyes were lost, grieving and she thought she was imagining the man who stood there. In two more strides he was at her side, an arm around her and the strong feel of it loosed her tears at last. A handkerchief appeared in front of he and she used it, was still using it as they walked back along the gravel paths from the dead, grey words and the flowers bright against the stone.

'I couldn't get here any sooner. The plane was late into Coolangatta,' Locke said in a low voice and kept on talking until her tears stopped. 'Did you drive?' he asked her and she shook her head, suddenly remembering the others. 'I came with Barry and Jan——' she looked up to find them all staring.

'I see you never mentioned me,' he murmured and performed the introductions himself. Quietly he talked with each of them, thanked Desmond for 'phoning him with the news. Everyone, even Gillian who was normally articulate whatever the occasion, was dumbfounded.

'I've hired a car. I'll drive you home.' Locke took Dru's arm. She kissed her brother and Gillian goodbye. Her sister whispered fiercely, 'What's going *on*?' but she just shook her head.

As he turned the car on to the highway, Locke began to talk, softly as he had before, telling her all that Sam had kept from her. He had been to Brisbane in his ancient suit that day not just to see his brother, but to hear confirmation of medical tests. Cancer. Three months at the very most they told him without treatment. He elected not to have it because he didn't want to gain extra time only to spend it in a hospital. Quality, not quantity Sam had wanted. His own tiny house, his fishing, his beach for the time he had left. When Locke said he would come back in November, he knew that Sam might have seen his last November.

'But why didn't he tell *me*?' she cried.

'Because he knew it would change the way you talked to him, make you feel guilty if you couldn't spend time with him . . .'

They fell silent, remembering.

When they reached Brisbane she gave him directions to her Annerley flat.

'What we both need is a Scotch,' Locke said when they went inside. She poured two. Locke tossed his back. There were pale patches around his mouth and lines beneath his eyes. 'I only knew him a couple of weeks but I feel as if I've lost an old friend,' he growled. 'Why the hell does life play such lousy tricks? Letting you meet someone like that so damned late——' He poured another drink and urged her to swallow some scotch.

'It must have been hard for you to get away,' she said.

'I was out of town. Only got the message this morning. But thank God I got back in time. I wanted to be here. Besides I prom——'

Dru sat up straight. 'You promised Sam?' She felt that sting again. The sting of pity. 'Did he ask you look out for me?'

'I'd like to see you happy,' Sam had said. And he'd guessed how deeply she'd grown to feel about Locke.

'Not in so many words,' Locke said.

'I'm twenty-three, Locke, and I will grieve Sam of course but I need nothing more than you've already offered. Your arm and your handkerchief back there. I'm grateful for those. I'm glad you came. But don't imagine that I'm so poor spirited I can't help myself— or that I have no one to lean on. I have.'

'Your family? Or have you patched things up with this Michael?' he asked, eyes narrowed. Dru tried to think what Sam might have said. He had warned Locke at first until he felt he could trust him. Had he then extracted some promise from him to keep tabs on her? And how could a nice man like Locke refuse the promise to a dying man? Sweet, loving Sam. But it cast her in the humiliating role of pitiable ingenue and Locke as reluctant guardian.

'I'm thinking about it,' she told him. If he thought she would return to her old relationship with Michael he could honourably forget anything he promised Sam.

'He's not here today,' he pointed out. 'Is he worth thinking about?'

'I've thought so for a long time. I told you I don't shrug off love so easily.'

'So he's had his fling and might marry you after all?'

'We haven't got that far.'

'How far have you got?'

She looked down, hiding her lack of interest in Michael, 'We'll just have to wait and see.'

Locke threw down the remainder of his drink and got up.

'I have to fly back shortly. Goodbye for now, Dru.'

'For now? You won't have to interrupt your schedule to check on me. I told you——'

'We'll be seeing each other. Sam altered his will. I tried to talk him out of it, but he was stubborn as a mule.' He reached for the door. 'He willed his house to us. Jointly. Next time I come up we'll have to talk about it.' He scribbled on a card. 'Here's my number. Ring me whenever you need me.'

Next time ... the words and the card got her through the sad days afterwards—got her through the small family gathering for her twenty-third birthday at which Barry warned her and Gillian questioned her about Locke. Her sister remained dissatisfied with Dru's repeated assurances that she barely knew him— that he had been at Sea Winds and was Sam's friend.

A few days later a reporter showed up on her doorstep, materialising out of the garden as she parked her car under the four storey block of flats. She managed to bluff him into thinking he had the wrong name when he asked her if she'd recently spent a holiday with Locke Matthews. It wasn't difficult. One look at her and the man was sceptical about her credentials as a Matthews mistress. She 'phoned Barry, then Gillian, and got their assurance that they had not spoken to the press and would not in future. Desmond McGinley rather stiffly said the same. He mentioned the will with disapproval but grandly declined to contest it.

After much nail biting and examination of her motives, she phoned Locke. It concerned him, she rationalised and he should know that people were asking questions. But deep down she admitted that she wanted to hear his voice. The admission made her abrupt and self-conscious when she got an answer.

'A reporter was here asking if I spent a holiday with you,' she said accusingly.

'What did you tell him?' He sounded amused. She could almost picture the smile and the matching glints in his green eyes.

'It isn't amusing, Locke. You might be accustomed to people nosing about in your—affairs, but I'm not. I told him of *course* I'd been with you . . . and I would tell him all about it if only the Earl of Lichfield wasn't waiting to photograph me wearing the Rothschild jewels——' He chuckled.

'It isn't funny. If this rumour gets around my friends are bound to hear about it.'

'Worried that Pennington might take exception?'

She hesitated. 'Well, it wouldn't look good, would it?'

'Has he changed his mind about you then?'

'Could be. It's none of your business. What I want to know is how that man knew my name and where I lived.'

His voice grew faint as if he'd moved away from the mouthpiece.

'—always very resourceful,' he said vaguely.

'Well if you get the chance, kindly scotch the

rumour will you? I have no wish to be tangled up in the sordid tales about your tedious affairs and secret marriages.'

'*That's* what I've been missing,' he said.

'What?'

'A taste of lemon.'

Her name appeared in conjunction with Locke's and all hell broke loose. Her workmates, still seeing her as Michael's jilted girl, alternately plagued her with questions and stared unbelievingly at the ordinary exterior that had been hiding a mistress of Mr Wonderful himself. Michael looked at her as if she'd been to Mars and back. It must have been a shock to see his reject apparently snapped up by a connoisseur. Reporters 'phoned her at all hours and waited at the flat to photograph her going to and coming from work. If she'd been gorgeous it wouldn't have lasted, she thought darkly. But she was ordinary and it made a much more intriguing story.

In frustration she 'phoned Locke.

'I can't stand this!' she shouted at him. 'Can't you do something? Tell them that you're nicely tied up with half a dozen nubile mistresses—tell them you don't have a taste for catalogue clerks. Not that I'll be one for long the way things are going.'

'Trouble?' he said with sympathy.

'You might say that. My boss isn't thrilled with my "notoriety". Neither are the tenants where I live. I could be out on my ear by the end of the month. And all because of you.'

'Poor Dru. I'm sorry.'

'You're not, you heel, are you? You're just glad it's taking the attention off you and the politician's wife——'

He didn't sound so lazily amused after that.

'Anything else I told the media would only make it worse, believe me,' he snapped. 'And that story about Dorothy and me was all conjecture as I told you.'

'Anything else—anything *else*? What *have* you said then?'

'For Pete's sake, Dru, it's a figure of speech. I've given out more statements to the press than you've had hot dinners. Calm down.'

'All right. I'm sorry. Naturally you wouldn't admit you'd been romping on the sand with me. It wouldn't exactly add to your image would it?'

'Don't talk like that.' There was a pause after the sharp words. Then: 'Have you been down to the beach since——'

Her throat tightened. It seemed just yesterday since she'd waved goodbye to Sam and driven away. 'No—I haven't——'

'Dru——' he said on a low, charged note of understanding, '—go there this weekend and I'll fly up. We have to discuss Sam's place anyway.'

'The reporters will follow you,' she said weakly. 'And me.'

'I'll give them a false trail to follow. Borrow someone else's car and cover your hair. That mop of yours is a giveaway . . .'

It was cold when she arrived at Sea Winds on Saturday. Seagulls circled over the beach, conditioned perhaps to appear for the early breakfasts Sam had provided for so long. Dru took her bag into the flat, then went on to the dunes, looking over at the grove of coast cottonwoods and the shadowed outline of Sam's house. What time would Locke come? She felt a leap in spirits at the thought of seeing him again. She would have to hold herself together. He knew she was fed up with the publicity but he must not see her depression. Whatever promises Sam had forced on him must appear unnecessary. It wasn't until she reached the trees that Dru saw Sam's open door, Her memory danced backwards. It was a reprieve. Any moment Sam would walk out, a piece of driftwood in one hand, a knife in the other and he would sit on the steps. 'Aaagh,' he would say. She hurried forward, logic warring with the wish. When a figure appeared in the shadowy interior she said, 'Sam?'

At the base of the steps she stopped. Locke came out, a newspaper in one hand and sympathy in his eyes.

'I thought——' she swallowed, gave a childish laugh. 'For one minute I thought you were Sam and it was all a dream. Isn't that the silliest——' her voice broke. Locke dropped the newspaper and came down to her, took her in his arms and rocked her.

'Dru, baby——' he murmured as she cried into his shoulder. When at last she calmed, she looked up and saw that look of compassion again. Pity.

'I should have brought Michael down with me,' she said, pushing him away.

'Dru—don't——'

'What—what do you mean?'

'His engagement notice was in the paper this morning with a photograph. I saw it just before you came. Why didn't you tell me there was no chance of him coming back to you. Was it pride, Dru?'

The tears flooded up again and he wouldn't know they were because she had no defence against him any longer. Michael could have a harem and she wouldn't care. But Locke would think she was spineless and heartbroken and she tried to tell him, but he hugged her and the words were muffled into his shirt.

'Darling Dru——' he muttered, 'Don't waste your love on him.' He was looking down into her eyes, she was gazing into his when the white glare of the camera turned their heads.

'Lovely morning, Mr Matthews,' said the reporter who'd first spoken to Dru outside her flat. 'Sorry I won't make you look as good as Lichfield, Miss Winters——' he grinned. 'Have I got the name right? It is Winters with an "s"?' Locke pulled her close against his side.

'No. It's Matthews with a double "t". Mrs Matthews.'

And less than a week later, it was. Mrs Matthews. Locke had let her storm and rant about it in Sam's house. Then when she ran out of words he simply said, 'I need you, Dru.'

Need. For her the word had a potency second only to one other. He needed her he said to save him from teeny-bopper fans and the press' endless speculations on who was in his bed. She needed him, he said now that Michael and Sam were lost to her.

'Did you promise Sam to look out for me?' she demanded.

'I didn't promise to marry you.' He grinned. 'But with your gift for words you'd be a riot in the part.'

She felt like hitting him then. He made it sound like he was offering her a role in a slapstick comedy. But his tone was serious when he went on:

'Marry me, Dru. We were friends here, we can stay friends——'

'What about—sex?'

He laughed at her bluntness, came and took her by the shoulders. 'By all means, if you want us to——'

She spun away. 'No—I mean. I don't know——'

'Nothing need change between us until you want it to. In time you'll forget Pennington——'

Poor Michael was already a memory. But she didn't say that. If Locke had said he loved her—if he had made his proposal less of a commonsense arrangement, then she might have told him. But pride would not let her show that for her it was not just a matter of need, but love. Why start off with a disadvantage like that?

Locke had so much on his side already. Even her own decision had been made as soon as she heard him say 'Mrs Matthews'. A stupid decision. A crazy, idiotic decision that cut across all her caution and commonsense. She could rave all day and it would make no difference.

'All right. I'll marry you,' she said masking her emotion in a rush of words. 'You realise everyone will think you've gone mad. The beauty and the beast they'll call us. No prizes for guessing which one is which.'

'Don't be stupid.'

'I'm being stupid agreeing to marry you. But I'll never get a more *handsome* offer will I?' He frowned. 'Having second thoughts already, Locke? Want to go out and call off the reporter? He's probably hanging about in the bushes hoping for some erotic honeymoon shots——'

'Dru——' he said on a warning note.

'It won't do *me* any harm. I can always sell my story to the Sunday papers—I almost married the Ransome Man—no, better still—I was held to Ransome——'

'Mr God you're a——' He grabbed her arm and swung her to him, looked fiercely down at her then laughed.

'Wait until I let you loose on them,' he laughed some more. As if she was a Dobermann Pinscher he planned to sic on his harriers. She cringed at the prospect ahead of her. His world was alien, peopled with the beautiful and the talented.

'I need you Dru,' he said again and he might as well have snapped handcuffs on her.

'I'll come quietly,' she said.

CHAPTER SIX

HER life was plunged into chaos. She resigned from the department and packed up her belongings in the flat. It was Sam who had reminded her that she'd once been the girl to take risks before the accident made her long for security. Well here I am, Sam, she thought— as she signed autographs for people who had scarcely paid her any attention but were now reminding her not to forget them and stay in touch—here I am taking the biggest risk of all.

Gillian got leave to travel with Dru to Sydney for the wedding. Her sister had adjusted to the fact that this farthest of all far-out men had been snaffled by the character of the family and not the beauty, but was frankly dubious about it. Barry was to fly down the next day with his family, to give her away. He was dubious too. That made three of them, Dru thought.

Their Sydney hotel was all mirrors, chandeliers and soaring vestibule and snooty desk personnel whose superiority vanished on hearing Dru's name.

'Instant grovel,' Gillian murmured in the elevator. 'Your intended has clout.'

'Locke's brother organised everything.'

'Hmm. I wonder if he looks like Locke. *Two* gorgeous Matthews men. No wonder the girls downstairs want to make friends.'

The suite was ankle deep in carpet, knee deep in flowers. Gillian read the names on some, 'I thought this was all going to be kept quiet? Some of these are from people in the States.'

Gifts arrived, telegrams and cablegrams—and dresses for Dru to try on, sent from a discreet little

Double Bay boutique. The hotel management sent someone regularly to ask if she needed anything. Fruit and wine in lavish supply.

'I suppose this is what you get if you pay enough . . .' Dru looked around at the alien territory of wealth.

'Cynical but true. I'm glad to see you still have two feet on the ground.'

Dru began to think that those two feet should run as fast as possible in a northwards direction. Her short 'phone conversation with Locke had done nothing to quell the rising panic. He couldn't come to her because that would only bring the press down on her all the sooner, he said. But he would send Eric to tell her about the arrangements for the wedding.

It was Dru who answered the door for the sixth time that afternoon. A man stood there, carrying a massive arrangement of orchids. She reached for the flowers, thinking him a delivery man. His stare stopped her. The orchids quivered in his grasp and Dru took an involuntary step back. She had a strong, illogical impression of anger . . . a wrong one it seemed, for he smiled suddenly and she knew who he was.

'Dru—great to meet you.' He laid the flowers in her arms and kissed her on the cheek. 'I'm Eric. I hope my kid brother told you I was coming.'

He breezed in, met Gillian with warm appreciation and then walked around as he explained the wedding details. He spoke very fast as if he was used to fitting five or six weddings into a day. '—cars to take you to the church—white Rolls. The drivers are experienced bodyguards——' he informed them, and—'I've taken the liberty of choosing the hymn *O Perfect Love* . . .' The roses and carnations swayed at the draught of his passing. Lacy gypsophila bounced about as in a gale.

He was not like Locke. Yet there were fleeting similarities. Similarities that must sometimes drive

Eric crazy, Dru thought. Nature had been a tease with Eric. Hair that was thick and red-brown on Locke was thin and redder on Eric. His facial bone structure was not unlike his brother's, yet the overlay of flesh was arranged too heavily for handsomeness. Eric was shorter, plumper and he had inherited the pale skin, the sandy lashes and brows of a redhead that Locke had magically avoided.

He stopped thought of something and snatched up the 'phone to snap out a few commands to the hotel caterer. The gypsophila trembled again as he whisked by.

It was Gillian who jotted down times and notes, Gillian who answered his questions. Dru sat in her chair, the orchids in her arms and felt oppressed by the luxury, the organisation, the pace—the very depth of the carpet beneath her feet.

'Will there be press at the wedding?' she asked. Her voice seemed to get lost among the flowers and the drapes and the carpet pile.

'We've kept the location quiet but there'll be a few. You *are* marrying a star, pet—so you have to expect it.'

Eric came over to her and took her hand. He looked into her face, blinked a few times. She felt the increased pressure of his fingers and again had that vague impression of anger. But he patted her captive hand and smiled. 'I'm glad for you both. And I know we're going to get along just fine, Dru. Welcome to the family.'

It was nice of him, if not entirely honest. He knew she was unsuitable. In his businessman's brain he was probably already totting up the terms of the divorce. Her voice jammed in her throat as she looked down at Eric's manicured hands holding hers. A ruby glowed in one of several beautiful rings he wore. An enormous ruby. It seemed to epitomise the gap that separated her. Locke's family and friends would all be ruby people. Maybe she could back out. It wasn't too late.

But it was. Much too late. Locke's mother arrived from Adelaide and she was delighted, friendly. Not one of the ruby people at all but tea and bikkies and unconditional approval. And she said the words that kept Dru from running away, 'He has needed a girl like you for so long.'

So Dru went to the stone church by the harbour and made her responses and came away a wife. And the photographers, who numbered many more than the few Eric had predicted, and the fans who had somehow gathered, muttered and murmured about the star's unlikely new wife. '—not even pretty, really——' she heard a young girl say in indignation. As if public property like Locke had a duty to be seen only with the beautiful. The cameramen and reporters loved it. It made better news that she was ordinary. Even in her new ivory dress and jacket, with her hair re-styled and tended by the hotel hairdresser, she looked average.

The reception was a blur to Dru. Only a handful of people were there—no celebrities, just family. Irene Matthews told her some amusing stories about Lachlan's early teen acne agonies and Eric's annoyance in later years at having his girlfriends distracted by a seventeen year old, acne-free kid brother—there were toasts made and the cake cut and camera flashes from the lone photographer brought in by Eric. Barry swapped motor bike stories with Locke, Jan stared fascinated at him and their two little girls shyly hung on to her skirts and watched him too. Eric's girlfriend Vanessa pouted while he made himself especially charming to Gillian as he went around re-filling glasses. Dru's 'gift for words' for which Locke had married her, had temporarily vanished. On this day none of her fast, smart remarks were appropriate. Eric filled her glass and talked to her. Bits and pieces of it penetrated the haze around her.

'. . . he's a great guy.'

She murmured agreement, her eyes straying to her husband who looked fantastic in a dark suit and a white shirt. '—a fascinating business we're in, Dru. But not easy—Locke and I have had a long, hard struggle to get where we are today——'

Locke picked up Barry's daughters, one in each arm to pose for a photograph. Laughingly he coaxed the children from their shyness with his natural, easy charm. A great guy.

'—tells me you helped him learn lines for *Man Alive*. Have you had any experience in the business?'

It was a courtesy question. No one in their right mind would think this dimwitted, mouse-haired girl had ever had the gall to get on a stage. She smiled. 'No. I don't know the first thing about acting or films or anything like that.'

If Eric thought that was a drawback in marriage to an actor, he didn't show it. In fact, as he stayed chatting to her, showing a warm interest in her very ordinary background, Dru came to the conclusion that Eric must be something of an actor too. For she could almost believe that he was genuinely reconciled to a plain, untalented sister-in-law.

'I won't mislead you, Dru—it won't be easy mixing it with the show people—not that you have to do much of it if you don't want to—but you'll have Locke and me to smooth the way. Of course he has to spend a lot of time away but I hope you'll always feel free to turn to me if you have any problems——'

Rather distantly Dru noticed that Eric seemed to expect her to have problems—he was right of course. She would. But she had a feeling her current stunned state was giving him the impression that she was a shy, timid mouse. Privately he must be baffled by his brother's choice. Her one redeeming grace—if her direct, sharp tongue could be called that—was gone for the moment and she was neither the beauty nor the character of the family.

'. . . fans won't like it,' Eric laughed. 'Prepare to be hated by thousands who wanted their hero to stay single and the image intact . . .'

But that was her job, she thought. His wife was to discourage the fans and give the press something less controversial to write about. But one day . . . Locke looked over and caught her eye. He smiled and started towards her, but the children, emboldened now, caught at his hands. One day, she thought smiling—she might mean more than that to him . . .

'—never thought he would marry again.'

Locke gave in to the little girls, crouched down to them.

Dru turned slowly to Eric.

'Again?' she said.

'Oh——' Eric pulled his mouth down, shot a thoughtful look at his brother, 'I just assumed he would have told you——'

'No.'

'It was a long time ago, before he made the big time. We never mention it in his bio notes anymore. They were married a bit more than a year—she died in an accident poor kid.'

'What was her name?'

'Eva.'

The press were drawn off by one of the showy Rolls to the airport. When it got there, a hotel waiter and a receptionist would get a celebrity welcome for a few minutes. There would be no honeymoon as such. Locke had his rehearsals and they would spend their first married months in his apartment. Locke drove them there in a four wheel drive Toyota. He owned a Rover as well he told her which she could use, but he liked tooling around in a 4WD. Tonight it was good camouflage.

'I've finally found a way to keep you quiet,' he joked in the car. There was an air of strain about him now that the festivities were over. She smiled but didn't answer.

'Are you regretting it?' he asked sharply. 'Thinking that he might have changed his mind if you'd waited?'

Dru looked up, startled. Surely he didn't imagine she was thinking of Michael?

'No, I'm not thinking that——' She was thinking that Eva's loss could still drench him in the cold sweat of nightmare and make her name a cry of agony on his lips. She was thinking that she'd known the risk when she married him—known that he needed her— hoped that he would one day love her. She was thinking that she might have to settle for need.

Dru rallied. Then need would have to be enough. The show must go on—wasn't that what they said?

'Actually,' she said, 'I'm wondering how you'll survive on my cooking.'

There was none of the tension she expected, living together—married, yet not truly husband and wife— she tried to help him with his lines again, he tried to teach her to cook. They quarrelled and laughed about both. They read each other the largely fictional accounts of their marriage in magazines and news-papers. The press, frustrated by a lack of access to the honeymooning star simply did their best with their imaginations and the releases given out by Eric.

He had vetoed interviews for a few weeks and Eric himself left them alone to fly to Mexico. According to Locke he made trips abroad as casually as some people caught a city bus, sometimes travelling twenty-four hours simply to stay somewhere forty-eight.

'Just two days?' Dru exclaimed. 'It hardly seems worthwhile.'

'Two days if the place has decent nightclubs—three if it has a racetrack and four or five if it has a casino as well,' he grinned. Dru shook her head. This was a world that occupied the 'What People are Doing Overseas' pages of magazines. The world of the beautiful people, the unusual, the talented and the rich. She wouldn't fit into any of those categories. Eric's secretary delivered a file of press cuttings culled from publications the world over. It was an ongoing job, monitoring the material used about a star and ensuring it was not libellous. 'Call it our publicity file if you must put a libel on it,' Locke quipped. Dru flipped through it amazed to find her picture alongside Locke's with Italian captions and even Japanese. She was glad she couldn't read them. The ones in English were lowering enough.

'Cinderella marries the Ransome Man——'

'After years of squiring the world's most beautiful women Locke Matthews marries a girl-next-door type——'

Harve Randall, a columnist known for his acid wit, suggested that the star was so fed up with an exotic diet that he'd decided on a change. 'From caviare to cabbage' was how he phrased it.

Dru began to see how irritating it was to be publicly examined. These writers knew nothing about her yet their readers would take their words at face value.

Locke's apartment was both beautiful yet in some ways modest for a man of his means. The furniture was more comfortable than elegant, the paintings a mix of traditional and modern, the lighting either concealed, shy spotlighting or explosive *Star Wars* chandeliers. A crammed bookcase and collected small ornaments from all over the world. There was a relaxed air about it. Atmosphere. It was the home of a genuinely nice man and it showed. But while he could afford so much more, Locke shared pool and sauna facilities with the other tenants in the apartment block. The position was close to town—easy access to the airport—right

around the block from Centennial Park's two hundred
and twenty hectares.

'I'm comfortable here—the other tenants don't
bother me and I could never be bothered moving,'
Locke said lazily. 'But we'll get something else if
you want to move. I own a few properties here and
there——'

She hastily squashed any idea that she might find
the apartment inadequate. Anywhere you are is fine
with me, she could have said. But didn't.

Mrs Curtis, who had been cleaning for Locke for over
a year, came in each day. She was a thin, angular woman
who said very little, perhaps because she always had a
cigarette in her mouth even while she vacuumed,
dusted and polished. She never dropped a flake of ash,
dividing her work unerringly between strategically
placed ash trays. Her skin was lined heavily as if
someone had traced a map, pressing hard with a blunt
pencil, and Mrs Curtis' face had been underneath.

She arrived one morning with her usual reconnais-
sance report of the street outside. 'That pair from the
T.V. magazine are out there again,' she informed
them. 'And a reporter fellow bailed me up in the
garage. Offered to put my picture in the paper if I'd
tell him all about you two—what sized bed you slept
on—and all that——'

She looked blandly at them. Dru flushed a little.
Mrs Curtis didn't look the kind of woman who would
be fooled by her freshly made bed every morning, or
the relatively smooth half of Locke's.

Locke frowned. 'What did you say?'

Mrs Curtis drew out a duster from a capacious
pocket and began doing the bookshelves.

'Told him if I ever saw my picture in the paper I'd
sue him.' She glanced at Dru. 'And I told him that
people's sleeping arrangements was no one's business
but their own.'

'Thank heavens for the incorruptible Mrs C,' Locke said later. 'Someone would probably keep her in cigarettes for a year just for giving the lowdown on our honeymoon.'

It was a strange, unreal time. Dru had little to do and was reluctant to go out alone and invite the press' attention just yet. When she discovered that Locke got up at an unearthly hour each morning to jog in the park, she waited a few days to be invited along.

'I want to come with you,' she announced one morning at last as he laced up his running shoes. He laughed at her defiant expression.

'I thought you'd never insist,' he said.

It was exhilarating. Their breath steamed in the frosty air. The sun lighted small treasures—the dew on a patch of clover, each drop magnifying its host leaf in iridescent magic—it back-lit a clump of long grass and shimmered down long, damp blades in a slippery slide to the earth.

A horseman passed by on the equestrian track and the warm smell of hide and hair and leather mingled with the fresh scents of morning. Locke stopped running and Dru breathlessly followed his lead in a series of calisthenics.

'I—never did this much——' she panted, when they ran on again. He looked over grinning, a faint sheen on his face but no sign of breathing troubles. 'Damn—you——' she stopped and bent at the waist putting her hands to her knees. 'You go on. I'll wait until you come back.'

She sat against a tree and gradually her body quietened to match the morning. A cyclist swished by, then another. Ducks and water fowl made plaintive cries and honks and way off, like a giant stirring, was the early hum of the city. She looked along the path. Locke had come back into view and she sat still, very still and watched him. His hair turned from brown in the flickering fig shadows to rich russet in the sun's open spaces. There was an easy grace in his movement, litheness in his big, muscular body in the tracksuit. Locke was close enough now for her to see his stubbly chin. He put off shaving until the last possible moment and when he did it, he used a Ransome razor—one of a truckload they'd given him, he'd told her—and foam from a shave stick. He always did the left side of his face first . . . so many ridiculous, unimportant little details she knew about him now. He still had clean sheets every day—he liked to drink his coffee when it was almost lukewarm—he worked hard at his physical workouts, like a demon at the play rehearsals and the pile of scripts in his study, but was too lazy to comb his hair before breakfast. He was warm and witty and generous and tolerant. But he could be impatient too—with the newspapers' guesses and misquotes and the frequent telephone calls.

'For God's sake, Sandy, don't ring me here——' she was surprised to hear him snap into his study 'phone one morning. It wasn't the first time the unfortunate Sandy had had the rough side of his tongue either. She'd felt quite sorry for the man on two previous occasions. On one of them she'd overheard his first impatient reaction before he broke off and saw her. She'd grinned when he'd asked her to close the study door.

'Not Sandy again? It's all right you know if you want to tell him off. I've heard rich language before.' Later he looked a bit shamefaced when she asked him if he'd demolished the poor man. Locke's anger never lasted long. It was another of the nice things about him.

His running shoes pounded out a rhythm. Dru watched him come the last distance to her and felt a sudden shaft of despair. Friends he had said they would be and they were. She rose to meet him. I love you, she thought, and it's going to kill me that you won't love me. He stopped, chest heaving under his brown jacket.

'So all that dashing about in your films isn't speeded up then?' she mocked.

'I can run fast enough to catch *you* darling.'

'Want to bet?' She took off across the grass, confident that she had the advantage now that she was rested and he still breathing hard. For a while it looked as if she might make it to the park gates before him but she looked back and he called her name on a warning note all at once. It was too late. She ran smack into a sapling and was thrown back on to the grass, stunned and out of breath.

'God, Dru—are you okay?' He knelt beside her, turned her head to touch the welt that was marking her skin, ran hands over the shoulder which had led into the tree. With an arm under her he scooped her up so that her head rested against him. 'Dru—say something——'

Hold me like this forever . . . she opened her eyes.

'I did it on purpose you know. To save your ego. You never would have caught me otherwise.'

There was relief in his green eyes and a warm affection that tore her two ways. Affection—how sweet and how wistful that could sound.

'Since when did you do anything for my ego?' he laughed and lifted her into his arms. Ignoring her protests and the stares of early commuters, he carried her back to the apartment.

They ran each morning after that. When a photographer appeared once, Locke ran behind a clump of trees and emerged the complete suburban man. He let his shoulders hunch and droop and leaned back a fraction. With his feet splayed outwards he looked the picture of middle age fighting to finish the distance in his morning jog. It was Dru who gave them away, doubled over with laughter.

It became a game. In the afternoons Locke went to the warehouse where he rehearsed for *Man Alive* sometimes until late at night but the mornings were theirs. Sometimes Dru wondered if she would ever have Locke's nights, but his mornings were undeniably fun.

'I want to buy you some clothes,' he announced over another of her disastrous breakfasts.

'No thanks. I've got plenty.'

'They don't suit you.'

'Are you saying I've got no dress sense?'

He deliberated, chewed on a charred sausage segment and swallowed it manfully. 'Yes.'

'And you have?'

'Of course.'

'Hmmpy. You played a fashion designer in your NIDA days I suppose?'

He dangled a wrist. 'Never. Get changed and let's go shopping.'

It was an experience, shopping with Locke. Dru enjoyed the subtle change in the saleswoman when they discovered that their unpromising customer had a sensational man in tow.

'Try this,' he said once and held out a garment to her.

'I hate it.'

'You'll look good in it.'

'My shoulders are too wide.'

'All that swimming.' But he didn't deny that her shoulders were too wide. 'Go on, try it.'

Of course it did look good. The saleswoman fussed over her, bringing in armfuls of clothes for her to try. Dru could pinpoint the moment at which she recognised Locke behind his sunglasses. The price labels shot into the triple figures.

Locke admired or criticised, and only once seemed impatient. He snatched a dress from the saleswoman and hung it up.

'Not pink,' he said shortly. 'I hate pink.'

Later he had another brief bout of irritability when, after splitting up briefly, Dru was a few minutes late rejoining him. She stared at his tight-lipped expression.

'For God's sake try to be on time,' he snapped.

'I'm only a few minutes late,' she protested at the childish outburst, 'What's the matter—can't the star bear to be kept waiting?'

'As always Dru—you've put your finger right on it,' he growled and took her arm in a ferocious grip. It was an unfortunate moment to be photographed by the vigilant press. The resulting picture of Dru looking plain and bewildered with the impatient, incredibly handsome star could only invite speculation on the quality of this 'honeymoon'.

But though not a honeymoon in the true sense it had its own special quality. They sailed on the harbour, drove to the Blue Mountains and shouted over Echo Point and Locke wore a disguise once so that he could take her unrecognised, to view the city from Sydney Tower. He put on a full, gingery-brown beard. A lush growth that framed his beautiful mouth and grew in nineteenth century importance to his chest.

Mrs Curtis took her cigarette from her mouth when she saw him. It was the equivalent of applause from anyone else.

'You wouldn't!' Dru gasped.

'I would.'

'Where did you get it?'

'Had it specially made. Saved all the clippings off my chest.'

'Read this,' he tossed an orange script binder into her lap one day at breakfast. 'I want to know what you think.'

'What I think? Locke, I don't know anything about screenplays.'

'You've got a sharp brain as well as a sharp tongue. And you're honest. If it's tripe I know you'll say so,' he grinned, reminding her of the first play reading she'd done with him. It was flattery of a sort she supposed. Her mind and her honesty were things he appreciated . . . and wasn't that what any red-blooded woman demanded nowadays? She read the script, *Brother Blade*. The leading role was a Locke Matthews one. Robust, dominating. Easily turned into a Ransome Man.

'I like it I think,' she said later. 'Will you do it?'

He thrust out his lower lip. 'Prentice is a sound role——'

'Travers is better.'

'It's a small part.'

'In the right hands it could be a great small part.'

Locke stared at her. 'I don't think mine are necessarily the right hands . . .' he said at last.

He gave her another script to read and another. Their discussions and arguments confirmed what Dru had suspected all along. Locke Matthews, successful, sought after Locke Matthews, had somehow lost sight of his real goals and now doubted his ability to play anything but the Ransome Man. She looked through his video tapes. None of his previous films were among them. Not too many people would believe that, Dru thought. An actor without tapes of his own films. She went to a library and hired a video of Locke's earliest film. The only one he'd made in pre-Ramsome-Ramage days. Dru was running it when he arrived home from rehearsals.

'What's this?' he said amiably as he threw himself into a chair. Then he recognised it. 'Oh boy—this was a rotten film to make. Six weeks on location up near the Birdsville Track. Bugs and dust and the flyaway tents I told you about. I vowed I'd have clean sheets every day when I got back to civilisation and made some money.' She smiled at that. 'What the devil are you doing with this anyway, Dru? It's ancient history. I didn't know what I was doing in those days——'

Dru glanced at him. 'You were acting,' she said.

Locke shuffled a bit in his chair. After a while he leaned forward, hands clasped between his knees. Dru got up and handed him the remote control and left him to it. For some time she heard him re-winding and running bits of the film again as he got re-acquainted with Locke Matthews, actor.

It was three weeks before he mentioned Eva. He was annoyed when she calmly said that Eric had told her about his previous marriage.

'I meant to tell you myself——' he said. 'It's just that I didn't really think it mattered after all this time.' It mattered too much, she knew that. That was why it had taken him weeks to speak of it. Locke could pretend but she had heard him cry Eva's name in his sleep, mourning her loss even after nine years. There were no photographs of Eva in the apartment. Dru was glad of that.

Eric called in at the end of the 'official' honeymoon. Dru was on the terrace when she heard Locke let him in. The brothers casually chatted about Acapulco and the Hollywood director Eric had run into and his jaunt over to Montego Bay on the spur of the moment. It was another world, she reminded herself and somehow she had to enter it and come to terms with it. This interlude with Locke had been wonderful but now she had to get used to the unreal world of the star. 'You'll have to go over to L.A.' she heard Eric say. There was a protest from Locke. 'The contract has a clause to cover it. They have to re-shoot those scenes with her highness in it. A week at the most if everything goes right.'

'Dru will come with me,' Locke said. 'Can we use your humble little Santa Monica hacienda while we're there?'

'Sure, sure——'

Dru's cheeks were flushed when she came inside, less from the idea of going to Hollywood than because Locke wanted her with him. Eric bounced to his feet, came over and took her hands and kissed her cheek.

'Hello pet—you're looking great, just great.' He beamed as she greeted him, then gave her arm a pat. 'How about some coffee, while we nut out a bit of business eh? Dru made the coffee, conscious of mild irritation. It was her fault she decided. Eric had every reason to believe she was the type to scurry to the kitchen while the men talked of important matters. He'd only ever seen her in a stunned state.

'I want to talk terms with Bradman over *Brother Blade*,' Locke was saying when she came back with the coffee.

'I knew you'd love Prentice.'

'I don't want to do Prentice. I want Travers.'

Eric was astonished. 'Run that past me again.' Locke ran it past again. 'Are you kidding? It's a supporting role. They've probably cast it already.'

'Tell Bradman I'm interested.'

'Hell Locke, they've got a decent budget but they can't shell out your kind of money for a supporter.'

'I'll do it for less.'

'A minor part for less money?' Eric gave an uncertain laugh closely followed by relieved comprehension. 'You're kidding, right?' He turned to Dru, 'The fan mags never do make enough of the star's sense of humour——'

'Being a star nearly cost me my sense of humour,' Locke said drily, 'Sometimes I think I'd be better off as an underpaid actor——'

'You've been there, done that. As I recall you didn't like it a lot.'

'Yeah—well, now I don't need the money anymore and maybe I'd like to stretch myself a bit.'

'Everyone needs the money old son. If inflation doesn't get you the taxman will,' Eric said dryly. Dru noticed him finger the ruby ring, rub his thumb across it like a superstitious gesture for luck.

'I've got nothing against being paid well—I'd be a fool if I did—but I want some parts with meat in them. God knows I haven't done any real acting for years.'

'Come on——' Eric laughed. 'That's crazy. *Ramage* won you best television actor award two years ago——'

'Eric, you and I know that all I do is play the same bloody role. Sometimes its dressed up in moleskins and whiskers like in *Nash's Gold* but it's all the same. I play the Ransome Man. Dru summed it up nicely. She said I do everything on film that was in the Ransome ads—except shave.'

Eric looked over at Dru, startled. For a second she had the feeling he was angry. But he laughed.

'Hey—everything but shave—that's good, pet——' Then to Locke: 'Let's keep everything in perspective. I know you've been getting bored, Locke, but who doesn't? Hell, I guess even Scofield occasionally gets bored playing his choice roles. After the play you'll feel refreshed, I know it. When you've gone through the heavy labour of live performances every night you'll be glad you're a screen man. Then we can get on with what you do best.' Eric spread his hands and waggled his head. 'And like I've always said, that's the secret in this business. Find out what you can do and do it just great. Look at Reynolds and Selleck. You start messing about, going outside your limits and you can end up a loser both ways.'

Dru frowned. Was Eric telling Locke he couldn't act anything but his stereotyped hero? Surely she must have missed something somewhere. Locke sighed.

'Maybe it's time I started testing myself again, Eric. Success kind of carries you along and you don't stop to think where it's taking you. I don't want to wind up in twenty years worrying about hair transplants and facelifts so that I can play an ageing Ransome. If I can break out I'd like to try it. I'm so stale and out of touch that I didn't even recognise the potential in Travers. Dru had to point it out to me.'

Eric glanced over at her again. His eyes were sharp, shrewd. He hid it well but she thought he wasn't entirely happy. She could sympathise. Eric was Locke's adviser after all and she wished Locke hadn't mentioned her in connection with his decision. But Eric bounced back. Literally. He was on his feet and almost prancing around.

'Okay, if that's what you want. I'll talk to Bradman. What about the *Conclusion* script?'

'I don't know, Eric. Once I would have jumped at it but——' he grinned, 'I think they only want me for my body.'

Eric shook his head and laughed. 'Just get this guy will you?' he said, turning to Dru. 'Here I am losing my hair, fighting to fit into my suits and this big lug sniffs at using his looks.' He shot a playful punch at his brother's midriff. Locke pretended to crumple. 'I tell you, life is unfair.'

Dru laughed at his doleful expression and left them to talk. Later when Eric took his leave, he put an arm around her and kissed her on the cheek.

'Did *you* read the *Conclusion* script, pet?'

'Yes. It seemed a bit spare on dialogue. More parts for cars and stunt men than for actors.'

'I'm surprised you could follow it—Draper's scripts are bloody terrible things.'

'I managed.'

'And you said you didn't know anything about the business,' he chided.

'Oh you know how it is,' she grinned. 'I don't know much about it but I know what I like.'

At Locke's insistence she joined him for lunch a few days later. As he was meeting Eric and a film executive she protested.

'Come on. I know you're not shy.'

'No. But it's all over my head.'

'It's won't be—not for long,' he flattered and she gave in. Locke certainly did appreciate her quick mind.

She knew she looked out of place in the restaurant, even in her new clothes. On Locke's arm she looked out of place anywhere, she thought—but here in the up-market ritz of the thirties re-created, she was all wrong. They were early and sat quietly over a drink while Locke told her about their guest, Graham McCann.

'On someone else's expense account he'll eat enough for two and drink two bottles of best claret single handed. Or single-mouthed. He has a lot of influence and a lot of contacts in the industry. He gets free lunches nearly every day,' he said drily.

Eric arrived with two girls clinging to him. They were voluptuous. Bosomy, blonde clones. A buzz started at his dramatic entrance. Eric shook off one of the girls momentarily to raise his hand and call out a greeting to the restaurant proprietor who had already spoken to Locke discreetly without drawing attention to him. Every head in the place turned to Eric.

'Martin old son, put my name on Thermidor here will you?' he indicated the live seafood tank where a number of lobsters cringed. Martin hurried over with a waiter to see Eric's choice and supervised the dismal business of netting the creature. Then he guided the two girls away. They went pouting, with hopeful looks over at Locke.

'We've got to talk business girls—order what you like——' Eric touched his fingers to his lips and blew them a kiss. As he made his way over he stopped twice to speak to other diners. He was beaming when he reached the bar.

'Dru pet, love your gear.' He kissed her, clapped Locke's shoulder and ordered a drink. 'My usual,' he said to the bar attendant.

It was a lunch such as she had never had. Graham McCann not surprisingly was an enormous man destined to become even more enormous. True to Locke's prediction, he ate enough for two and drank enough for all of them. Eric consulted the waiter and then the chef over two of the dishes discussing them at length—there was a constant coming and going at the table, of other guests who knew Eric well and Locke—judging by their eagerness—not as well as they would wish. He smiled and talked in his own relaxed manner—almost under-stated by comparison with Eric. Ironic really. One man had the look of the star but not the manner—the other had the manner but not the look.

'*Darlings——*' A perfumed, scarved, bejewelled vision floated to a standstill at their table. Eric got up and greeted her.

'Philomena you look fantastic—come on, tell me where you found the fountain of youth.'

She laughed, accepted a rather winy kiss from Graham, who almost missed the mark and turned her full attention on Locke. 'Ah, you big brute——' she sighed as he towered over her and bent to kiss her cheek. 'When I see you I wish there was a fountain of youth. If only I was thirty again . . . .' Philomena said in the throaty voice of a woman who knew that once she'd been desirable. Dru recognised her. Philomena, whose other name had vanished somehow, had hosted celebrity talk shows, written countless columns in women's magazines, dabbled in fashion and any other arena where her outspokenness and unique appearance were plus factors. She was rumoured to be over sixty and her past was suitably mysterious and European flavoured. Once she was beautiful—the remnants of the beauty were still there framed in chokered pearls and outrageous auburn hair. Her make up was as thick as her accent. And her eyelashes were thicker than both.

'But think of the people who would drink from a fountain of youth,' Locke murmured as he beckoned a waiter for another chair. 'Harve Randall, for one.'

Philomena's false-fringed eyes flashed. The acid tongued columnist, Dru observed was not one of this lady's favourites. She said one or two succinct things about Randall, rendered less offensive by her accent, but nevertheless frank enough to set Dru back in her chair. Philomena cackled, reached out and grabbed one of Dru's hands in her own beringed one. The strength of her grip and the metal of her rings made the sensation powerful. Like holding hands with the bionic man. 'So this is your wife, Locke my darling——' she looked long and hard at Dru, who said 'Hello.' It sounded dreadfully inadequate in such colourful company.

'Now don't tell me what is your star sign——' she commanded and closed her eyes for a moment. Her lashes rested halfway down her cheeks, Dru noticed in fascination. 'Cancer or Leo I think——'

'Cancer,' Dru admitted. 'But how could you tell?'

Philomena waved a hand and a hundred jewel facets flashed. 'I tell,' she dismissed.

'Are you still on this horoscope kick Philomena?' Eric laughed. 'I don't believe in any of it——'

'You should believe, Eric,' she sent him a sly look. 'It might help you win on the horses sometimes——' Eric reddened and tossed down his liqueur.

'Cancer——' she mused, regarding Dru steadily, 'Sensitive and loving and sometimes hiding like the crab,' she reached out and touched Dru's heavy mass

of hair, 'but you have the crab's pincer. You hold on—
so.' Her hand tightened and Dru only just managed to
repress a grimace. 'When you are threathened—so you
hold on. No running away from the bad times for
you.'

Dru gulped, looked down at Philomena's glittering
red-clawed hand. 'Why do I get the feeling that you
are Cancer too?'

The woman cackled again and let her pincer grip
loosen. 'I like her,' she announced to the restaurant at
large. She insisted on having Dru's birth date to
prepare a horoscope chart. Then on a round of kisses
and a billow of silk, she departed.

'You must do a chart for me one day, Philomena,'
Eric called after her. 'Silly old cow,' he muttered when
she was out of earshot. 'Time she retired. But
Elizabeth Arden would probably go out of business if
she did.'

Graham took a cab then the three of them went to
the carpark. Eric's racy red Porsche was parked near
Locke's more sedate Rover. Once again Dru smiled at
the irony.

'—the new *Ramage* series,' Eric was saying, 'From
what Graham told me, we can screw them down to
whatever we want, which is what I thought——'

'I'm not sure that I want to do any more *Ramage*,'
Locke said thoughtfully. 'I know it means losing out
on a lot of publicity but——'

Eric jerked to a halt. He had the look of a sleep
walker who wakes to find himself on a slim parapet.
'You can't give up *Ramage*. You've never mentioned
giving it up——'

Locke didn't notice his brother's pallor apparently.
'It's been on my mind since I went on holiday,' he
said. 'Do you think I should do another series, Dru?'
he asked her as if her opinion was valuable to him. It
was a heady feeling but Dru thought it would be

tactless to venture advice with Eric watching. Her brother-in-law looked almost stricken. *Ramage* was clearly a project close to his heart.

'Well—you know I don't personally like the show but I don't know enough about the business to offer opinions on whether you should take it on again.'

Locke nodded. 'There's time yet. We'll kick it around a bit.'

It was clear that she was included in that 'we'. Dru was dismayed at Eric's quickly disguised resentment. She didn't want to come between Locke and his brother.

'Right. We'll do that,' Eric said and motioned the carpark attendant who dashed over and reversed the Porsche out and drove it the short distance to where they were standing.

'When do we have to go to Hollywood?' Locke asked.

'The week after you finish your theatre contract. Opening night next week—any nerves, old son?'

'Plenty. I have a feeling that the critics are going to rip me limb from limb.'

'You would insist on doing a play.' Eric shrugged. 'You'll be there opening night, Dru?'

'Of course she will. It will be Dru's first official appearance as Mrs Matthews.'

'Don't lose any sleep over it pet. It's a jungle out there but you've got us. Now don't you worry, hear?'

Dru, who hadn't worried at all up to then, felt a flash of anxiety.

Eric said goodbye, kissed Dru and went to the throbbing car. The two blonde clones appeared again, fluttered their lashes at Locke and slid into the Porsche, giving a fine display of bosoms and thighs. The attendant and several other people turned to watch the car take off with an exclusive roar. They watched Locke too and Dru couldn't help feeling that it must be a disappointing sight. The star driving off quietly with an ordinary wife instead of two showgirls.

'You know I think your brother is more a Ransome Man than you,' she said.

'He certainly shaves more often,' Locke chuckled.

CHAPTER SEVEN

DRU could not toss off a vague disquiet that appeared to be separate from her yearning to be a real wife and a loved one. She couldn't pin the feeling down. But one thing emerged more certain than ever, over the days that followed. Her love for her husband grew stronger the more she knew of him. And she wished she could make the move to go to his bedroom and tell him that now she wanted to be more than friends. It was the mirror that stopped her. One look in it and she knew it had to Locke who made that move. If she could not be loved, she had to at least know that she was wanted.

'Tonight,' Locke said to her at breakfast on the day the play was to open. She met his eyes with a leap of excitement and apprehension.

'Tonight—what?' she croaked.

A smile curved his beautiful mouth. 'Tonight we drink that bottle of French champagne I put on ice a month ago.'

'In celebration of the beginning of the play?'

'In celebration of the beginning.'

That night she sat in the theatre with Eric and Vanessa.

'How do you like the play?' the girl said to her at the interval. 'You don't seem to be laughing much.'

Dru almost blushed. Her eyes had rarely left Locke, her mind had not registered the play—it had been busy with a scenario of her own preference . . . Locke had set two champagne glasses in the refrigerator that afternoon . . . she had draped a new silk nightgown on her bed before leaving . . .

'That's because I know it almost word for word. I

helped Locke learn his lines.' She smiled. 'I had awful trouble reading glamorous divorcee Rhonda's part.'

Melanie Cross, who was playing Rhonda had no trouble with it. The play unfolded smoothly and Locke who had been tight with nerves that afternoon was relaxed on stage. Dru overheard any number of surprised comments on his comic acting ability and she stored them away, picturing herself relating them to him as they drove home. Home. Laughing, they would walk arm in arm to the elevator. Perhaps on this second beginning Locke would carry her over the threshold of the apartment. Would he kiss her then? Dru watched the stage and wondered about that. If he doesn't, she thought—I'll kiss *him*. She bit her lip at the idea of taking the initiative . . . then nodded. Yes, she definitely would kiss him if he didn't kiss her first . . . then . . . she would change into her silk nightgown and . . . would he come to her? Or would she go to his room? Perhaps they would both emerge from their rooms together and collide as they had that morning at Sea Winds. She stifled a nervous giggle. What would he wear? Pyjama pants low-slung, a brocade dressing gown like in the movies—nothing at all? . . . they could laugh and Locke would take her in his arms, caress her through the silk . . . the champagne would be in a silver bucket by his bed, the glasses already filled and fizzing . . . as they drank, Locke would look at her with those fabulous green eyes and he would put his glass down . . .

Applause.

. . . and slowly, very slowly he would reach out for her . . .

'Aren't you going to clap?' Vanessa asked.

. . . and she would touch him and love him . . .

The curtain closed on the play and on Dru's private preview. Just in time, she thought laughing softly, and joined the applause.

Afterwards they went backstage where Dru was introduced to the cast. They were more curious than anything and surprised. So she really *is* ordinary she could almost see them thinking. It didn't matter. She had a celebration to go to tonight.

Locke left her with Eric and Vanessa and went to change. Somehow as Dru dodged the purposeful stage crew, she lost the other two and stood uncertainly near the dressing room doors. Vanessa's laugh came from one of the rooms, but still Dru hovered, disliking the idea of making an entrance into a room full of theatre people. The clear, carrying voice of Melanie Cross, who was better know for some idiotic T.V. soup commercials than for her theatrical roles, kept Dru where she was.

'—maybe she has hidden talents. But there's no doubt he's played his cards just right. All that devotion to a homely little wife has killed the Falkland story and——' she paused, '—will keep the spotlight off him and Sandy.'

'Sandy? Is she still in the picture?' another woman asked.

She? Sandy—a woman? Dru stood transfixed.

'Is it still on between them?' the woman insisted.

'Lord, you've seen Sandy and you've seen his wife. What do you think?' Melanie gave a brittle laugh.

'Melanie,' Eric objected weakly, 'This is all rumour, pet——' There was more. Gossip, careless and relished. The discussion dropped in volume as if they suddenly remembered that the 'homely little wife' was in the general vicinity. When Eric emerged and caught her eye, Dru walked quickly away.

There were reporters waiting by the stage door when they left. Some of the cast, including Melanie walked out with them. But Locke was the target. A photographer snapped him and Dru.

'Mrs Matthews, what do you think of the play?' a reporter asked. It was an inane question that invited a standard answer. Everyone looked at her. She stood there feeling her despair harden to a cold core of anger. Not only was there a loved previous wife, but a mistress who 'phoned and 'phoned her married lover. And Locke had let her think Sandy was a man and a nuisance and all the time he was probably arranging their next meeting. All those late, late rehearsals. But for what? She glanced at Melanie Cross who wore an indulgent smile at the hesitation of the homely little wife.

'The play? I think it's tripe,' Dru said clearly and there were several gasps including one from a reporter. 'But beautifully done.'

Locke almost threw her into his car. His modulated voice rose to lambast her for a full five minutes without pause. 'Why? Why the hell did you have to say that? Are you some sort of saboteur?'

'I said what I thought.'

He ranted again. When they got home his anger showed no sign of abatement. Hands on hips he glared at her. 'You've probably rung the death knell on the play with that crack.'

'Oh rubbish! How could my opinion influence anyone?'

'Because you are my *wife*, you stupid little idiot——' he grabbed her and shook her so that her tight curling hair swayed about her face.

'Wife! Ha! You married me to give the press something respectable to write about you for a change. You wanted to see me "let loose" on them, to put it in your own words. Well now I've *been* let loose—tough if you don't like it.'

'You think all I want from you is your smart back-chat?' He gripped her arm and strode to his bedroom. She resisted, remembering how she'd pictured going there in silk and in naïve acceptance that she would lovingly fill second place in his heart. Second? Go to the end of the queue, stupid.

'Oooh, is this the big scene?' she mocked. 'Shouldn't you have your shirt off for this—you always do in your movies.' He pulled her along behind, swung his arm at full stretch then let go so that she tottered into the darkened bedroom and landed on the bed.

'Bull's eye,' she gasped, her heart knocking holes in her chest, 'You got the leading lady on the bed in one take——'

'Shut up.' He leaned over her, one knee on the mattress edge, a hand fast in the crinkled mass of her hair. With a wrench of his wrist he angled her head for his kiss. All his shock and fury at her disloyal criticism were in it. He had come to expect the little wife to say and do the right thing in this odd marriage of theirs. Dru reminded herself of that while his lips bruised hers, reminded herself that he had lied to her and let her go backstage tonight where everyone knew she was a joke as a wife.

Dru dragged her head free.

'What finesse!' she flung at him. 'My first boyfriend kissed better than that and he was only twelve——' she sucked in her breath as Locke swept a hand over her, rumpling her skirt up over her thigh, tugging her chiffon blouse from the waistband to bare her midriff. He pushed beneath the fabric to fondle her breast.

'Is that so?' he whispered in her ear. His fingers worked their way under her bra. With the utmost finesse now, he stroked and plucked. 'Perhaps he was a bit young for this . . .'

The sensations were exquisite. Dru couldn't stop her sigh of pleasure. Oh no. She twisted her body to escape his touch. It was worse—wonderful and worse. Locke let her sit up then caught her from behind.

While she flailed harmlessly at him he unfastened her blouse and nuzzled at her neck. 'And this—how about this . . .?' he murmured and put his mouth to her nape while he curved his hands to her breasts. No. Her head sank back against him. It was getting more difficult to remember the thought she had to hold on to. Don't . . .

'Dru darling,' he muttered and swung her about. Her hands went to his shirt, began undoing the buttons. His chest was bare and smooth. How beautiful he was to touch . . . what was that thought? Don't ever . . .

Locke pushed her blouse over her shoulders, slithered it down her arms. He unhooked her bra and stroked its straps aside too. The zipper of her skirt opened to his touch—his tender, expert touch. Locke took a long time to dispense with the skirt, touching and caressing her as it slid over her hips and thighs . . . desire knotted inside her. He could make her want him so easily—but he knew that, didn't he? He could have his beautiful girlfriends and then, anytime he chose, he could make love to a wife who knew she was getting the leftovers. Her arms went around his neck. I love you, you rotter. But it's not a good enough reason. What was that thought? Don't ever settle for . . .

'Dru—sleep here with me—I want you.' The weight of his body settled on her. Her skin flamed. 'I love you darling.'

Second best. Don't ever settle for second best. Sam had said that. Second best would have been good, Sam. Not perfect—good. But third best? No. She made her body stiff, inhospitable. 'I love you . . .' She wondered how many times men had trivialised those beautiful words at a high moment of sexual persuasion. Not even 'I love you, Dru' but the nice, impersonal 'darling'—the all purpose endearment safe to use should you get your lovers' names mixed in the heat of moment.

'I don't want to sleep here with you,' she said, turning her head. 'But you married me so technically I suppose you have the right to insist. I hope you won't.'

There was a stunned silence.

'What the devil are you talking about?'

'You said nothing need change between us unless I wanted it to,' she reminded him. He switched on a beside lamp. Stubbornly she held his gaze. 'I don't want things to change.'

'What was all that writhing about then?' he demanded harshly. 'You touched me as if you wanted to make love.'

'What do you expect? I'm only human after all. Physically you're very—appealing.'

His handsome mouth parted as if to say something then snapped closed so hard that a muscle clenched in his cheek.

'But it just wouldn't be right for me, Locke. Mere sex—without love——'

He looked away from her. There was an oddly vulnerable look about him. Hurt. 'I thought—over the last few weeks—it's Pennington then is it?'

Michael? She'd forgotten Michael. Locke caught her by the shoulders. 'Do you still love him? Do you?' he insisted when she didn't answer. Eva and Sandy, she thought—and who else? But he had the nerve to want her to wipe out any past allegiances.

'Yes,' she said at last and he let her go.

Locke was morose and monosyllabic the next day. His only reference to the previous night came when he opened the bar refrigerator and took out the two frosted glasses.

'I'll leave the champagne on ice,' he said dryly, 'Who knows, you might change you mind.'

A tiny piece in the morning paper featured her comment about the play. And a critic quoted her.

'As the leading man's new wife—clearly not too starry eyed to have lost her critical ability—said—it is tripe, beautifully done. I can put it no better than Mrs Matthews.' Days later it became clear that neither her comments, nor the critics' had affected the play's popularity but Locke's mood showed little sign of improvement. Which was unusual for him.

Eric called in, eyes flicking from Locke to Dru.

'Now you're not going to hold that comment against her are you old son,' he said in a jollying tone. 'After all, Dru hasn't had any experience with showbiz. It was probably just nerves.' He winked at her and she squirmed. He was trying to be helpful but somehow it made her sound immature and a bit simple.

'It hasn't done the play any harm,' Locke said with a glance at her, 'So let's forget it.'

Eric smiled. 'You sure dropped a clanger pet, but as time goes by you'll get the hang of it.'

But maybe Eric was more annoyed about her 'clanger' than he appeared. He didn't kiss her either when he arrived or left this time.

Locke remained distant until the following Saturday. Dru went out on to the balcony to water the pot plants and was greeted with a chorus of boos from the street, six floors below. To her astonishment the noise seemed to come from five nuns, grouped on the pavement and staring up at Locke's apartment. Very young nuns, she thought from what she could see, wearing make up and somewhat outdated habits. Locke wandered through the living room to the kitchen in his low-slung pyjama pants and morning stubble. His hair was standing on end and he scratched one shoulder. It reminded her of the first morning she'd run into him at Sea Winds.

'You've got some admirers out there,' she told him.

'Are they in costume?'

'Habits.'

'Oh boy, this I've got to see.' He went to the balcony doors with her and peered down. The girls saw him and cheered. He shook his head and laughed. 'They must spend a fortune hiring outfits. Once they came in spacesuits.'

'Was that what you meant when you said some of your fans had seen you first thing in the morning?'

Locke looked down at her. 'Yes. Did you assume I meant a closer view—like from the next pillow?'

'Well—I suppose I did.'

'Not me. I've never been a groupie man.'

'They booed me. How long do you suppose they'll stay there?'

'Last time they waited until I went out. About three hours. Tore my best shirt as I got in the car.' Thoughtfully he regarded Dru. 'Of course there's an ironclad way to get rid of them, probably for good. But I'd need your help.'

'That's what I'm here for isn't it?' she said, 'To repel your teeny bopper fans? And stop people talking about who is in your bed.' Which was ironic. The one person definitely not in it was his wife.

'Come on then.' He grabbed her arm and pulled her out to the balcony railings.

'If you're going to pose for them you'd better scratch your chest or something ungodlike to put them off—they can't see the ginger stubble on your chin and the mess your hair is in from there.'

'I'm not going to pose for them,' he waved a hand at the girls, '*We* are. Wave to the fans, dear.' He took Dru's hand and raised it. The fans fell silent. Then he swept Dru into his arms and gave her the big screen treatment. Stared into her eyes for a few moments and kissed her, moving his mouth generously on hers, rubbing her lips apart for a deeper tasting.

'Mmmmm. Orange juice,' he murmured against her lips.

'Count yourself lucky. I nearly had grapefruit.'

'I like grapefruit too.'

'What about lemon?'

He laughed and his breath gusted, mingled with hers, 'Lemon I'm used to. No—don't go.' He held her tightly against him when she made to leave, brought her back to his hard muscled warmth until her lips were touching his again. 'We haven't finished.' Again he kissed her and this time she wrapped her arms tight around his bare back and returned the kiss. Second or third best—it didn't seem to matter right then.

'There,' he said with satisfaction and looked over the balcony to the street. The fans in their black and white habits had gone. 'That worked very well.' He surveyed her from head to toe and nodded. 'Thanks, Dru.'

It was the end of his moodiness, thought they didn't again achieve the camaraderie that had so marked their honeymoon days. She saw little of him. With few exceptions he slept late after his performances and spent the afternoons working out at his club or reading in his study. It was the end of morning jogs in the park. The end of quite a lot Dru thought unhappily. Once, after an hour of restless pacing around the apartment, he asked her to play squash.

She almost beat him. Almost. As a member of a B Grade team in Brisbane she had played some pretty tough opponents, but Locke was superbly fit and clearly using the game to rid himself of excess energy. They left the court panting and gleaming with perspiration.

'You're good,' he acknowledged with a respectful glance at her. The little wife was okay as a sporting partner. His praise twisted inside her as she thought of Sandy.

When they drove home, he said: 'How about a spa to ease your aching muscles?'

'Great.' She wore a bikini.

'You can take it off if you want,' Locke told her, 'We've got the place to ourselves.' It was a small room with planters of giant leaved philodendron and an Italian tiled floor. Leading off it was the door to the pool and the sauna—the door that Locke had fastened against any other tenants.

'No thanks.'

'You don't mind if I do?' he said as if he was asking if he could smoke a cigarette. Dru waved a nonchalant hand.

'Go right ahead.'

He wasn't simply teasing as she thought. He casually stripped off his trunks, watching her all the time. She was already in the spa, being pummelled by the surging water, and stubbornly refused to look away. The redness of her face she reasoned, could be accounted for by the heat of the water.

'What are you waiting for?' she asked, as he stood stark naked on the spa's edge. 'I'm not going to screech in ecstasy or swoon just because you've got your britches off.'

Locke eased his muscular frame into the water. Closing her eyes she leaned back and let her body lift on a jet of bubbles. The halter neck of her bikini bit into her neck and she raised her arms to loosen it.

'Take it off,' Locke said and her eyes flew open. He was right beside her. With a casual twitch he untied the strings of the bikini and pulled it from her, catching her about the waist when she tried to snatch it back. The hapless bra top flipped on to the tiles and Dru struggled to be free. She disappeared under the water for a second and was heaved up in strong arms, spluttering and cursing him.

'Tch, tch, where did you learn language like that?' he teased and held her slippery body to his to sink down into the warm, fragrant water. He let her go then and at first she wasn't sure if he was touching her or if it was simply the water massaging her body.

'Don't——' she said as the unmistakable touch of his hands registered on her. Green eyes half closed, his mouth slightly parted, he watched her as he closed his hands over her breasts, kneading and squeezing with his thumbs and long, strong fingers. She gasped, tried moving away but he followed until she was on the ledge that ran the perimeter of the pool, well below water level. Her back was against the side and she twisted, but the steaming, surging water planted her on the seat in exactly the right position for Locke. He caught her legs between his own and continued his sensuous exploration. Dru's hands slipped over the skin of his shoulders as she pushed at him. Droplets gleamed on his golden skin and rolled slowly down . . . her hands lingered, her eyes drooped. Locke's caresses were indivisible from the water's massage. His hands moved down beneath the bikini pants to tweak at the ties and the soaking garment joined its other half on the tiles before she quite knew what had happened.

'Oh—you . . .' Dru circled the pool, gripping the sides as a jet threatened to raise her above the surface. 'Go away——' He caught her, stilled her protests with a kiss and eased his thighs between hers. 'No,' she mumbled against his lips at the touch of his intimate, probing hands. The steam clouded—the water jets drove fiercely into her . . . 'Locke——' she cried as the heat and the need became unbearable.

He let her go, retreated to the far side of the pool, legs stretched out. 'Refreshing isn't it?' he said and studied her incredulous, frustrated face.

'You—you——' she said when she got her voice back. 'You did that on purpose——' He'd used all his expertise, aroused her to want as she never had before, taken her to the very edge . . .

'I could hardly do it by accident,' he mocked. 'You

only have to tell me if you want me to go on.' His voice deepened. 'No? Another time perhaps.'

She got out of the pool.

'You look superb naked. Like a beautiful athlete.' Locke said and she snatched her towel from the tiles and slung it around her. 'You won't mind if I don't come out just yet, will you? Things have er—altered—since I came in and I wouldn't want to embarrass you.'

Dru cast him one look and hurried to the door. Locke's laughter echoed after her. But it seemed to her that it cut off before the door shut behind her.

The play drew to a close. Locke had contracted to play only the first month of its run. Another actor would take over for the remaining Sydney season and take it on tour. Locke would have a week off when he finished at the theatre then he would go to Hollywood to re-shoot some film scenes marred by the presence of an actress who had been replaced by another later in the original filming schedule. He was going alone now. Eric's house, he told them apologetically, was occupied by some friends who were staying longer than he thought. Locke explained that it wouldn't be much fun for her staying at a hotel while he worked but Dru knew that it was her apparent gauche comment about the play that had changed his mind. He and Eric couldn't take the risk of having an outspoken, naïve, plain wife on show in Hollywood.

'What will you do while I'm away?' he said from behind his newspaper at breakfast one morning.

'I might go up to the beach house. I'd like to see that Sam's place is okay.' They had arranged for an agent to check it out periodically until they decided what to do with it.

'Pull it down,' he'd advised them. 'It's a fire trap anyway and not worth a cracker. The land is valuable though and would be worth more but for that creek and the swamp near it.' The extent of Sam's property had surprised Dru. She knew his cottage had stood on a sizeable block but hadn't realised that, apart from Sea Winds, Sam owned all the land along the beachfront. He must have resisted offers to live his simple life from choice and alone and she would never know why. He could have been rich. Her eyes were faraway. She thought of Mrs Pennington's comfortable, beautiful Ascot home and its heartless atmosphere. In a way Sam had been rich.

'Dru——' Locke reached out and took her hand. He searched her face the way he did whenever she remembered and felt the loss again.

'It's all right. I was just thinking about Michael's mother's house and how——' she stopped as her hand was crushed momentarily in his grip.

'Put Pennington out of your mind. He forgot you easily enough.'

'No, that's not what I was——' she began to say but Locke cut her off.

'I don't want to discuss him or his mother. And I don't want you staying up at the beach alone. It isn't safe.'

'You think some uncouth character might break in in the middle of the night?' she said sarcastically. 'Mistake me for someone else?'

'If you go it will be with me,' he said, unmoved.

We'll see about that, thought Dru.

She drove him to the airport. By some system known only to themselves, the press knew of his departure and were waiting for him. Locke swept her up in his arms in one of those love scenes he did so well and she forgot that she was acting a part for the entertainment pages and T.V. magazines. Then he was gone, reluctantly leaving her to the mercies of the press who were a little more insistent and a lot less polite without his presence. She was, after all, a nobody, raised to prominence only by marriage. Eric was supposed to have been here to keep them at bay but there was no sign of him yet.

'Some people feel you're an unlikely pair Mrs Matthews. How do you explain your marriage?'

'I don't.'

'Why did you marry him?' How did Locke keep smiling through these inane questions? Dru mocked surprise.

'Why? For his mind of course.'

A patter of laughter. 'What the fans would really like to know is why did he marry *you*?'

'Isn't it obvious? For my looks, naturally.'

More laughter. Dru began to walk and they followed her. Eric hurried towards her, all apology. He firmly stopped the questions and as he whisked her away gave her a curious glance. 'You seemed to be holding on your own.'

'Didn't you think I could?'

'Frankly no. You must be made of sterner stuff than I thought. I need to talk to you Dru, pet. I'll follow you home.'

Dru couldn't have said why the sight of Eric's red Porsche in her rear vision mirror made her uneasy.

Mrs Curtis was at work, oiling the leaves of the pothos that had created a jungle in a corner of the breakfast room. When she'd made coffee for them, she went back to work on the plant.

'Could you do something else?' Eric said rather sharply to her. She threw him a dour look. Her cigarette tilted in her mouth as she left the room.

'I guess you overheard Melanie at the theatre that night,' he said as the vacuum cleaner started up. Dru stiffened.

'I meant to get you alone before this and tell you Sandy's nothing to bother about. Nothing at all.'

He covered her hand with his. Dru looked down.

No ruby ring today, she noticed in a detached way.

'Believe me, Dru—it's rumours, nothing more than that.' He was protesting a great deal, she thought and met his eyes. Eric's slid away. 'Of course,' he said, 'I admit they had a thing going in the past ...' he cleared his throat. 'But I just know he wouldn't have had anything to do with her since then.'

'Is she an actress?'

'No pet—Sandy Craig is a model—she's on the cover of one of the fashion glossies this month.'

After a short silence he said: 'Hey, Van and I are throwing a party tomorrow night. Why don't you come?'

'Thank you, but——'

'Say no more,' he held up his hands. 'You think Locke mightn't like you going out without him, right?'

Her chin snapped up. 'Wrong. I'd like to come. Casual or dressy?'

'Anything goes pet. There'll be a few big names there if you know what I mean ...' He patted her arm. 'Tomorrow night then, Dru. Around eight.'

After he'd gone Mrs Curtis switched off the cleaner and returned to the pothos. Half the leaves glistened from her attentions, the others were dull.

'I'm sorry Eric was so sharp with you, Mrs Curtis.'

'No need for *you* to apologise Mrs Matthews. He's not one to waste his time on them that don't count.'

'You don't like him.'

Mrs Curtis wiped the excess off several leaves. 'Too much oil,' she muttered. 'It's not for me to like or otherwise. But its a pity he's not more like our Mr Matthews instead of acting like somebody out of a film.'

CHAPTER EIGHT

ERIC'S house was a splendid architectural arrangement of tiers sprawled down a rocky slope at Whale Beach. He lived there a few months each year when he wasn't in the States or England negotiating on Locke's behalf. At present Vanessa lived with him. Dru wondered where all the blondes fitted in.

Eric had a nose for moneymaking investments Locke had told her. He had acquired some very valuable properties for them both in the last few years. And not just properties. As Eric took her to the noise of the party they passed fabulous spotlit sculptures and paintings, glass cased antique pieces. Dru stopped at a triptych of blown up photographs that occupied most of one sweeping wall. Three studies of Locke— the action man, tattered shirt over oiled muscles—the playboy wearing a dinner suit and promise in his eyes—the adventurer in bush shirt and moleskins.

'I always thought stars had pictures like these in their own houses,' she joked. 'Locke doesn't have any.' Eric smiled but didn't answer as he led her past the three faces of the Ransome Man. He opened a door and warm air blasted her. And music. There was a babble of voices and a scatter of colour around the aqua dazzle of an indoor pool. Movies were flickering silently over the far wall beyond a tangle of tropical plants and people danced, sat at tables, posed on sun lounges. Through the splash of several swimmers Dru noticed one thing in common. Everyone was wearing swim or resort wear. The long sleeves of her sapphire blue dress were suddenly hot and tight. It was, she had thought, a really nice dress even if it had lost some of its promise after she'd bought it. In this setting, it might as well have been fancy dress.

'You should have told me it was a pool party——'

'Pet, I'm sorry—didn't I say?'

Dru turned clear grey eyes on him. 'No. You didn't.'

He groaned. 'My mind's like a sieve lately. Van gets furious with me.' He walked her to the bar and poured some wine, 'Drink this, pet, and forgive me.'

He took her on a round of introductions. 'My sister-in-law,' he would say and introduce the other guest along with a resume of his/her accomplishments in the business. Dru smiled and sweltered in her blue dress, feeling her disadvantage. Her sole claim to individuality appeared to be her marriage to Locke. The guests were friendly and most unconsciously patronising to the mouse-haired girl who couldn't even wear the right gear.

Vanessa emerged from the pool and wrung out her waist length hair, looking askance at Dru's dress.

'Oh, don't you swim?' she asked. Dru felt the girl had held back an 'either' at the end of that question. Illogically she felt a spurt of anger. Had Eric said to her—Locke's wife doesn't seem to have any talents—I can't think what he sees in her? Well of course he had. It was exactly what most people would think—she'd known that from the start.

'There are a couple of spare bikinis and towels in the dressing room if you're too hot,' Van offered.

Dru decided she would change immediately before she melted. But on her way to the dressing room she looked up at the movie wall and saw Locke. He hacked his handsome way through bamboo jungle, stopped to fight off hordes of almost naked natives, swung from a vine over a gorge into a miraculous, luxurious bathroom. There was no sound but she saw his lips move in the famous catch phrase 'And if you think that was a close shave . . .' He shaved, aided by a busty blonde—another clone like the ones Eric had decorating his arms at the restaurant—and settled, suave and elegant into a wing-backed chair with a cigar, brandy and the blonde. It was one of the Ransome ads. Another of the series followed and Dru watched, admiring Locke yet wondering why she felt faintly repelled.

'Not blue, darling—you should *never* wear blue.' A man stood near her. He was reed-slim, wearing a jump suit open nearly to the waist with an aviator scarf flung over one shoulder. Mort Flanagan, he introduced himself. Set designer, interior decorator, artist, sculptor and writer. 'And those are just a few of my talents,' he admitted.

'I confess I haven't heard your name, Mr Flanagan,' she smiled. 'And if I had I'd be inclined to think it was that of an all-in wrestler or a boxer.'

Mort laughed. 'With a name like Flanagan you wouldn't normally be far wrong. I come from a long line of brawling Irishmen. Of course,' he inspected his pale fingernails, 'I'm not—ah—typical of my family.'

Reluctantly, she excused herself to change for the heat was oppressive in her long sleeved dress. All the spare bikinis looked as if they'd been designed with Cannes cameras in mind. Dru chose the one with the most fabric and wrapped a towel around herself, hoping that now she would simply blend in with the crowd. Mort strolled over to her when she emerged again.

'Going in, Dru?' Eric called out across the plants. Dru turned to find almost every eye on her. She might not be shy as Locke pointed out but she didn't relish this kind of mass attention. 'Go on pet, take the plunge—if you can't swim Gale will rescue you.'

Laughter greeted that. Some 'in' joke apparently.

Dru felt a rank outsider. Gale came over to test the water. She had on a leopard skin patterned swimsuit that was cut high, high over the hips so that her legs looked endless.

'It's warm,' she said kindly to Dru. 'And shallow up this end if you don't like getting out of your depth like me.' She sauntered off and slipped into the shallow end near the steps, looking back from the centre of the pool with a jungly smile.

'Oh dear, oh dear, I think our Gale is going to be a bit bitchy again,' Mort murmured and glanced at Dru, 'She—er—had a bit of a thing about your husband a long time ago. He took her out a couple of times when she worked in a *Ramage* episode. Just between you and me she had hopes of a long liaison on and off screen if you know what I mean. Gale has ambition but not a whole lot of talent—love your suit, Gale darling!' he waved to the girl in the pool and mimed a kiss. At Dru's askance look he said, 'I know. I'm a dreadful hypocrite. I only get away with it because I'm talented and entertaining.'

'And modest,' she said drily. Another ex-girlfriend of Locke's. The world was studded with them apparently. And not all ex's.

'And modest,' he agreed just as a piercing scream came from the deep end. Gale's head bobbed above the water then she sank only to appear again bubbling a pathetic—'Help—it's dee-eep——'

Dru dropped her towel. She didn't stop to wonder why a self confessed fraidy-cat should be in the deep end. Just as she dived in she heard Mort say, 'No, darling, don't—she's acting again——' But it was too late. Intrepid Dru was in the water and feeling an absolute fool as Gale surfaced again, laughed at her would-be rescuer and feigned more panic to the amusement of the onlookers. Dru had a vision of leaving the pool—herself the butt of an old joke and

Gale, once a Locke Matthews girlfriend, wearing her jungly smile. She put her face down in the water and powered the length of the pool to the girl. She wanted to be rescued, so rescued she would be. Gale seemed a bit nonplussed when Dru reached her so quickly and grabbed her under the arms. She even struggled a bit and disappeared under the water in an unrehearsed flurry.

'Don't panic,' Dru said soothingly, 'Otherwise I'll have to hit you.' It was so tempting. Gale, still resisting a bit but no match for Dru's superiority in the water, was towed to safety. Obviously her set scene had never included rescue—not by a woman at any rate. She was pouting when she was hauled up on to the poolside by some of the onlookers. Dru pulled herself out and stood over her. 'Do you think she needs resuscitation?' she said anxiously and Gale leapt to her feet.

'It was a joke,' she snapped. 'I'm a good swimmer— I wasn't drowning.'

Dru opened her eyes wide. 'Oh, weren't you? You made it look so *real*.'

Several people laughed and eyed her with speculation. Mort murmured, 'Are you sure you haven't had any acting experience?'

'You've certainly had plenty in the water. You can really swim, lady,' someone else said.

'My father taught me,' Dru said and ruthlessly tossed her father's name in among these celebrities. 'Wes Winters.'

'Well, for heaven's sake,' a peeved Gale said as the conversation hung around Dru's father's prowess and her own. 'If they make another Tarzan movie you've got a real chance. You've got the shoulders for it, darling.'

Dru grinned and eyed the leopard swimsuit. 'I might have to borrow your hide though.'

It was a small triumph. Very small. Dru was absorbed into the party yet remained conscious of a prickle of uneasiness. Eric circulated in his bouncy fashion, talking about motor racing here, skin diving there, about Monte Carlo and the Bahamas. And on the wall Locke paddled down white water, fought off two burly villains and escaped in a hot air balloon manned by another blonde clone . . .

'I didn't know you were such a super swimmer pet,' Eric said later as he saw her out. They were in his foyer—a sweep of marble and glass with a bronze sculpture and a spotlit abstract painting of immense proportions.

'Perhaps Locke told you and you just forgot. That sieve of yours,' she reminded him. His gusty laughter followed her to her cab. He'd forgotten to kiss her goodbye again.

But Mort Flanagan hadn't. He'd given her a card with a friend's name on it and told her to go see him about her hair. 'And don't wear that ghastly blue again darling—peach or apricot or beige. Not blue.'

Mort's friend called himself simply Drakos. He had a gaunt, olive skinned face and fierce, black brows. In one ear he wore a diamond stud. Drakos sat her in a chair in a private booth and walked around her for maybe five minutes. Twice she started to say something but he said 'Sssh,' and kept viewing her as if she was a piece of stone he planned to sculpt. He ran long, thin fingers energetically through her hair then clicked them and had her taken away to the basin for a shampoo. When she came back, wet hair slicked back he allowed himself a nod and began cutting. He never asked her what she might like and Dru closed her eyes when she saw great, crinkling falls of hair sliding down the silk coverall. At length he whirled her chair around to the mirror with the air of a magician whipping aside a veil.

'There. Now we see you.'

Dru gulped. We certainly did. Her hair was shorn to an inch all over her head. Suddenly she had eyebrows and cheekbones. There was a young, vulnerable look to her. She felt naked and put her hands to her face. Drakos slapped them down and snapped his fingers again. Another girl took her away to a lay-back chair and began working on her face. Mort Flanagan, she thought, if this goes wrong you'd better summon up your Irish fighting blood. But it didn't go wrong. It went amazingly, incredibly right.

Her brows, thick and several shades darker than her hair which now looked more caramel than mouse, had been sparingly shaped. The eyes that had always seemed small framed in an unmoving mass of hair, had grown larger. Even their colour looked right. Grey, she saw in surprise, was not such a dull colour. It was warm and sparkling. Her nose was as ordinary as ever and her mouth was still too wide but she had come into focus in some odd way.

'Drakos,' she said as she left, 'You are a genius.'

'But of course,' he said in surprise and executed a bow.

Mort's friends she saw, were as modest as himself.

She flew to Brisbane for a few days and visited Barry and Jan and the children. They were delighted but almost uncomfortable with her new image. As if she had rejected the role for which she'd been cast so long ago. Gillian was less surprised when Dru caught her with an hour to spare between sleep and schedules, 'I always knew you could be an eye-catcher if you found the right look. And you've found it.' She gave her a letter. 'I was going to mail it on. It looks like Michael's handwriting.'

It was. Dru read it, feeling a certain unreality. To think that once she had anticipated spending her life with Michael.

'What's it about?'

'He'll be in Sydney soon. He gave me his hotel number,' she smiled, 'Michael wants me to have lunch with him.'

'And will you?'

Dru cast her an amused look. 'Of course not.'

In defiance of Locke's wishes, she went to Sea Winds from Saturday night to Monday. Rather belatedly she painted the sign and hung it up, reflecting that she would have saved herself a great deal of torment by doing it long before. Then she couldn't have sent Shelley away and Locke would never have stood with her under a million stars in an April sky . . . was that the night Sam had told him he was dying? Perhaps that accounted for some of the pity in his eyes when he'd kissed her.

The beach was September lonely and Sam's house a narrow, threadbare reminder of Sam himself. On Sunday she took some flowers to his grave and sat there for a while to remember all the other wordless times she'd spent with Sam. Unlocking his place before she left, she looked around. The sextant and chronometer had gone to his brother as was proper. All his worthless treasures were still where he had left them. The driftwood dragon was there, waiting in vain for Sam to make it static. She picked it up. It turned from a fire-snorting monster into a pretty shape as she tilted it. Underneath were the tiny letters cut into a fold. SILLA. She put it back with Sam's other things. There was dust and sand settled on all the surfaces and she spent some time cleaning it away. A futile gesture she knew which brought a few tears. She locked up and walked quickly away. She was on the plane before she remembered she had not brought the dragon with her.

Dru went to meet Locke's plane a day later. She wore a new caramel coloured outfit that warmly toned

with her once-mousy hair. Another visit to Drakos'
salon had unlocked the secrets of make-up for her and
now she could apply just the right touches to
emphasise her grey eyes and soften her wide mouth.
Gamin—the beautician had labelled her. She found
that funny. And she wondered what Locke would
make of the change.

She was surprised to see Eric first. Apparently he
must have flown over to the States too on one of his
lightning trips. He was resplendent in dove-grey and
burgundy tailoring but it was Locke behind him who
was attracting all the attention. In canvas pants and an
open-necked shirt, sweater slung over one shoulder
and in need of a shave, he was unfairly eye-catching.
When he saw Dru, he blinked a few times then smiled
his heart-stopping white smile that drew a few sighs
from nearby women. Dropping his bags he pulled her
into his arms and ran a hand over the soft, curling pile
of her hair.

'You've been shorn.'

'Do you like it?'

'I like it.' The warmth flooded through her,
depressing her again. Pleasing him was all too
satisfying. 'Glad to see me?'

'I don't know,' she eyed his stubbled chin. 'You
might at least have shaved on the plane.'

He laughed. 'Now I know I'm back home.'

She liked the sound of that. If she didn't know
about Sandy, she would be dreaming foolishly that he
meant it. Eric whistled at her new appearance.

'You look great pet—who did you go to?'

'Mort's friend, Drakos. He told me about him at
your party.'

When Locke stepped aside to sign an autograph
Eric said in a low voice, 'I'm glad you took Mort's
advice. Locke was hoping you would.'

Her smiled dimmed. That explained Mort

Flanagan's interest in her. Had Locke asked him a favour—When you meet my wife, give her a few clues about improving herself—see if you can make her presentable?

Eric came back to the apartment with them. He stayed an hour while Locke filled her in on the problem-beset shooting of the past week.

'I've got a possible buyer for your beachfront property. Did Locke tell you?' Eric said to Dru and she stared. Had Locke handed over Sam's place to Eric's care without even consulting her? Locke stirred wearily, put his hands to the back of his head and stretched. 'We didn't really discuss it, Eric.'

'Just as well,' Dru's tone was militant. 'I'm half owner don't forget and I don't want to sell.'

'The house is an old shack from what I can gather——' Eric said, 'I spoke to the agent and he said it was a pile of junk—a real temptation to vandals. You could do a good deal on the land though even with the drainage problems near it.'

'I don't want to do a good deal,' Dru said shortly. 'That pile of junk belonged to a—a friend and while it stands the land will remain as he wanted it.'

Eric leaned over and patted her hand, smiling at her as if she was a good child who'd suddenly thrown a tantrum over a lollipop.

'Okay, okay—I'm just trying to look after things for you both. But face it, that old place is just going to fall to pieces one day if it doesn't go up in smoke first.' It was about then that Dru admitted to herself that she didn't like Eric. She had tried—really tried. But somehow Eric was always associated with bad news. 'You and your family should consider selling Sea Winds,' he went on, 'You could buy a decent condo in Surfers with the money.'

She glanced over at him, confused by a host of fleeting recollections none of which she could grasp.

But she had to make allowances. She could dislike anyone who conjured up images of Sam's cottage falling to pieces.

He went on to remind them that Locke was to dine with a producer that night and to fly to Melbourne the following evening.

'What did you do while I was away?' Locke asked when Eric had gone. He picked up the magazine she had left oin a coffee table. Sandy Craig's beautiful, pastel face was on the cover. Locke froze momentarily when he registered the photograph—he glanced briefly at Dru then casually flicked the pages and tossed the magazine down again. Ever the actor. Somehow she had hoped he might tell her about Sandy when he saw it and confirm Eric's claim that she was past history.

'Called your mother now and then,' she said coolly. 'She's coming to visit for a few days soon. And I took some cooking lessons, went swimming—the pool is rather cool yet.' She didn't mention her weekend at Sea Winds. If it came up she would defend her right to do as she pleased but right now she was too dispirited for argument. Locke slept for the rest of the day and when he came back after his dinner engagement that night she was in bed. She didn't move when he opened the door of her room. A few moments later he went away again.

But he had the dream and she went to him and held him and murmured words of love and comfort until he slept in peace. As she went back to her own bed, she wondered if Sandy had ever been with him when he called Eva's name in the night. She smiled bitterly at the idea of Sandy knowing that she was only second best.

The next night he flew to Melbourne accompanied by Eric to talk terms for another *Ramage* series. Contrary to his intentions Locke had not discussed it with her again but she sensed that he had gone cold on the television show. So she was surprised when Eric came back alone two days later and dropped by to tell her that Locke was doing another season.

'All he has to do now is sign the contract,' he told her.

'Oh, by the way he'll probably stay over another couple of nights.'

It hurt but it was really no surprise. Harve Randall had reported Locke's visit to Melbourne in his column that day. 'Is it just coincidence that the *Ramage* star and an old friend of his happen to be in Melbourne at this particular time?' he'd written. Dru had wondered which 'old friend' it was. Now she thought it was probably a model with beautiful, pastel colouring.

'Have you given any more thought to selling your beachfront land, Dru? That buyer is still interested.'

'It isn't beachfront land to me, Eric,' she said snappishly, still thinking of Locke's extra nights with his 'old friend'.

'Sentimental value, eh?' he nodded. 'But let's be realistic pet. Take the house away and what have you got? Real estate.'

'You sound just like—someone I used to know. He said practically the same thing.'

'Sounds like a man I could understand.' Eric grinned shamelessly. 'I'll bet he's going places.'

'Oh yes—I think you could say that Michael won't be held back by sentimentality.'

'Michael . . .? There's a story there somewhere. Old boyfriend, pet?' he teased.

When he had gone, Dru paced around the apartment. No doubt Locke and his old friend would be very discreet. They might not even leave his hotel room in case a photographer happened along. Then he would come home to his wife who was keeping the gossips at bay with her new, respectable presence in his life. Dru fumed a little, paused before a mirror and stopped, mildly surprised as she always was at her new appearance. She put a hand to her hair and smiled slowly. Defiantly. Then she fetched Michael's crumpled letter from her bag.

Dru wouldn't have been human if she hadn't enjoyed Michael's reaction. He stared at her as she approached him in his hotel lobby. Perhaps it occurred to him that she might have been equal to the task of ambitious man's wife after all. Several people turned to look at her. She held her head high and enjoyed it. She was getting used to the fact that it wasn't just that she was Mrs Locke Matthews, but that she had acquired a certain lookability of her own.

'Dru—you look wonderful,' he said rather weakly as they went into the hotel restaurant, and she wondered how he would describe her to his mother. Or if he would at all.

'It's just gloss Michael. I'm still the same underneath.'

It was a fairly boring lunch. When they had exhausted the topics of departmental departures and promotions, mother's new decor and his fiancée's arts degree there wasn't a lot left to say for Dru wouldn't discuss her life with Locke.

'You know, Dru,' Michael said at last, 'I'm beginning to think I might have made a mistake about you. I miss your humour, you know that?' He covered her hand with his own.

'I came up quite nicely with a bit of help, didn't I?' she said drily and he reddened. 'You didn't make a mistake, Michael. You were absolutely right. We would never have suited. We'd just let ourselves drift into the habit of being together.'

She patted his hand. And that was how the cameraman photographed them. The man took off before either of them could stop him. Dru shrugged.

It wouldn't worry *her* if Locke should see it. He couldn't have one rule for himself and another for her. Michael was more upset.

'There was always the risk of publicity—you must have known that when you asked me to meet you,' she said unable to feel a whole lot of sympathy. 'Your fiancée will understand. And your mother.'

She didn't think Michael would look her up again, somehow.

Eric burst into the apartment two days later almost knocking Mrs Curtis off her feet.

'Locke's back from Melbourne. He's down in the spa,' Dru told him.

'Is he out of his mind?' Eric snapped.

'I don't think so, Eric. He often takes a spa bath.'

But he was not amused. 'Have you been giving him more of your advice, pet?' he snarled. Dru didn't know what he meant and said so. She was shaken. Eric looked as if he hated her.

'He's knocked back *Ramage*, that's what he's done . . .' his face was contorted. 'How could he do this to me . . .' He took a deep breath and rushed out again, presumably to find Locke.

'Are you all right, Mrs Curtis?' The woman had stepped hastily back to avoid another collision with Eric. Otherwise she seemed unperturbed and unsurprised. Her cigarette rested securely in the corner of her mouth.

'He's a bit upset,' she remarked in understatement. 'Must be worried about the money.'

'Money?'

'His percentage of the T.V. show fee.'

'I don't think so. He's worth a fortune,' Dru said repressively. It didn't seem the thing to discuss her brother-in-law with Mrs Curtis.

'A fortune is never enough for them that gamble. He's sold off a few things lately. My hubby works for an auctioneer . . .'

Horses, Philomena had said. And Locke himself said that his brother loved casinos and racetracks. Eric lived a high life. A house in Santa Monica, one here—his art collection and his blonde collection—cars. Jewellery no doubt for the clones and poor Vanessa. Top restaurants and nightclubs. Yes, Locke's decision could be a financial disappointment to Eric but somehow it didn't seem an adequate explanation for the hate she'd seen in his eyes.

He must have had his fury under control by the time he saw his brother in the spa. Their discussion certainly did not appear to disturb Locke for he came upstairs later and merely said that Eric had invited them to his place the following night for a party.

'Do we have to go?' Dru asked, unable to forget the look on Eric's face.

Locke stiffened. His mood had deteriorated following his return from Hollywood. And his extra nights spent in Melbourne had improved it only briefly. When his bear-hug greeting had not elicited any response from her he had been persuasive, teasing.

'There's no need for all this, Locke,' she had pointed out: 'There are no news people around to impress with your new domestic image.'

His mood had been sombre since then. 'This isn't a business engagement. But if you don't like my brother enough to accept for pleasure, regard it as part of the duties you like to quote.'

'I—don't dislike Eric——' she began, her conscience pricking her. She did dislike him but it was such an illogical thing that she tried not to give it credence.

'Make an effort, Dru. He has noticed your coolness to both himself and me.'

Vanessa exclaimed at Dru's changed appearance. Her eyes darted over Drakos' expert haircut, noted the strapless apricot dress that exposed the too-wide shoulders in shapely elegance.

'I *am* dressed properly for the occasion this time I hope, Eric?' Dru joked. 'I brought a change of clothes and a swimsuit just in case.'

Eric gave his gusty laugh and patted her arm. But it wasn't the correct dress he'd forgotten to divulge this time. It was the guest list. Dru sensed something right away. Locke stiffened beside her. Eric muttered something apologetic.

'She came with Charlie,' Dru heard him say, 'Honest old son, if I'd known——'

A tall, pastel blonde made her way over to them with catwalk grace. Her figure was sexily slender. She looked at no-one but Locke. It was Sandy Craig.

CHAPTER NINE

'DARLING,' she pouted and took both his hands. 'You really *are* married. I suppose I'll have to congratulate you.' She did. On the mouth.

Eric caught Dru's eye during the congratulations and raised his hands in a helpless gesture. 'Sorry pet,' he mouthed the words to her with such a look of remorse. It was familiar, that unconvincing look of apology. Unconvincing. Her mouth dried a little. How odd it was that this was the second time she'd been embarrassed at Eric's house. The other guests all knew about Sandy and Locke. She could see sympathy in their eyes for her as she stood beside her husband and the over affectionate model. With all her new look, Dru was aware that the comparison disadvantaged her. Eric watched her. Eric—and bad news. It had happened too often. This meeting was no accident. The conviction came suddenly and close on it a jumble of other things to support it. She looked away but Eric's gaze still touched her. It made her neck tingle. Like the night she'd stood in the dark on the stairs and known something or someone was waiting for her.

Locke disentangled Sandy and wiped away the pastel marks of her congratulations. He put his arm around Dru in a husbandly gesture.

'My wife Dru—this is—Sandra.'

It was really quite funny, Dru decided. Locke was trying to bluff it out. With a bit of luck his wife might not associate this beautiful Sandra with some nuisance male character called Sandy. And if she hadn't overheard Melanie he might have got away with it.

'Oh "Sandy" please—no-one calls me Sandra darling, you know that.'

Dru derived a certain malicious satisfaction at her husband's sudden rich colour.

'Sandy,' she smiled delightedly. 'I used to have a puppy called Sandy.'

Locke steered her quickly away.

'It isn't what you think,' he said in a low voice.

'I can see that,' she replied. 'She's a girl for a start.' Several people came up to them. Dru was introduced to a quiz show host, a musical arranger and an orange haired singer. Melanie Cross popped up with a thin, balding man in tow. More 'darlings' and kisses for Locke.

'Hello, Dru,' Melanie said, all eyes and assessment for Dru's new un-homely image, 'You'll remember me from the play.'

Dru certainly did. 'I—think—so,' she said, unflatteringly slow to place her, 'But I do enjoy your soup commercials.' Locke whirled her away again. What an embarrassment his outspoken wife was! Tough!

Philomena made an entrance, all silk wisps and pearls with a liberal dusting of diamonds. Her auburn hair was, if anything, redder and more bouffant. She had a long cigarette holder which she brandished to successfully cut a path through the guests to Dru and Locke.

'Oh life is cruel!' she cried, putting a beringed hand to Locke's cheek. 'Every time I see this face I want to be young again . . .' He bent down obligingly to her diminutive height and she kissed him. Philomena reached for Dru's hand as she had before. Her nails were silver this time. 'Darling—hello—I haven't finished your chart but I must warn you to be on your guard. Your stars show a period of great unrest. Watch for someone who is not what he seems.'

Dru smiled wryly at that. 'In this business, isn't that everybody?'

Philomena cackled. 'She learns, she learns——' her fingers squeezed tighter and she leaned forward. 'But it's there in your stars. Someone waiting. All in the dark yet . . .'

Dru felt a chill up her spine at the repetition of her own thought less than an hour ago. 'But, you hold on—the pincer—yes?' The beringed hand bit into Dru's. 'And *do* be careful about fire, won't you, darling . . .' she waved her cigarette holder at someone and whisked away. Dru grimaced and brushed a bit of hot ash from her arm. Well, she had been warned about fire, she thought with a smile. But—someone waiting . . . it sounded like the title of a psycho movie. Dru repressed a shiver and addressed a passing tray of wine. She drank it and snatched at little bits of conversation:

'Locke—is it true you might be the next James Bond?'

'My dear Dr—no.'

'—well, you know Jack. He's a terror for punishment—*two* of them——'

'—one more try at importing a yank for the lead but Equity will be savage——'

'—in France?'

'No kidding. Couldn't find a decent white wine. Had to drink beer—a matter of survival, mate.'

'—with a name like Mad Max. So I turned it down . . . Mel did a great job though. He's not just a pretty face——'

'Lorrae darling—you look fan*tas*tic——'

And so the evening went. Darlings and honeys and extravagant praise, sarcastic witticisms. A woman got up and sang, unasked and unaccompanied and for the most, unapplauded. A male guest wandered in wearing only drawstring shorts and body paint.

Locke stayed with Dru, the picture of the attentive husband. But she and everyone else she supposed, knew that he wanted to make sure his wife and his mistress didn't get together. But they did anyway.

Dru was in the guest room touching up her make-up when Sandy came in. There were two other women there too. They glanced apprehensively from the model to Dru.

'Oh my God,' Sandy cried at her own image in the mirror, 'I look ghastly.' Which was something of a put on. She looked fantastic and knew it.

'I should look so ghastly,' one of the other women murmured. Sandy brushed pastel colour on to her cheeks and smiled at Dru in the mirror. There was a noticeable gleam in her eyes. 'This must all seem so strange to you, Dru. This kind of party I mean.'

'Not really. I went to the circus a few times as a child.'

The other women smiled. Sandy paid some attention to her eyes, using another tiny brush to apply blue shadow.

'I mean—you must feel a bit like Cinderella, marrying someone like Locke.' She gave a merry little laugh. 'You'd be wondering all the time if midnight was going to strike.'

'Well, she might apply her make-up with tiny little brushes Dru thought, but she used a shovel for her spite. It was cheering to know that Sandy was jealous. Ironic too.

'Why should I worry about midnight?' she grinned. 'When it strikes I get to go home with Prince Charming.'

Sandy had to do her lips twice before she left. The other women followed. 'Bravo, Cinderella,' one of them said.

But her defences were getting ragged. Dru delayed her departure as long as she could. When she went out and saw Locke's red-brown head above the others on the terrace, and a pastel blonde one nearby, she turned tiredly away from the party into quieter corridors. She stopped for a time in front of the triptych of Locke. Eric was an art and celebrity collector, host and jet-setter. Without Locke he would still live well—Eric would always do that she thought—but he would be on the fringes, the outskirts of the business he seemed to love. Locke looked down from the wall, his magnificent physique sexy in the tattered shirt. Was that why Eric didn't want his brother to turn down his macho starring roles and the television series?

She moved on, went into a sunroom furnished with lacquered Chinese couches. On the wall were shelves filled with beautiful, natural treasures. A split thunder egg, its agate core polished to a marble sheen, a burst of amethyst, sea-shells and urchins. Dru picked up a shell and ran a finger along its smooth, high-gloss curve.

So many years of playing similar roles had eaten away at Locke's confidence to do anything else and it looked as if Eric had played on it. When the signs of restlessness became all too dangerous had he arranged the sop of the lightweight stage role in *Man Alive*? If so, it could have been a mistake. Locke's ability in comedy had received some attention since then. The image of the Ransome Man had been shrugged off a little with that exposure. And with the acquisition of a wife. Dru gazed unseeingly at the shelves. A wife who unwittingly bolstered the star's attempts to break away from the big time and the big money if necessary to do the work he wanted. Less money. How astonished, how upset Eric had been at the thought. How quickly he had hidden his annoyance when Locke had shown his respect for his wife's opinion. Eric, she thought, was over-estimating her influence. Locke had been discontented and ready to change direction before she

met him. The important thing was that Eric must have
seen her as a catalyst. For it was plain now that he had
taken steps to sour the growing understanding in their
marriage. Nothing much—little things. But effective
in a marriage even more infant than Eric knew. A
word here. A hint there. Consolation that always left
her feeling inadequate and suspicious. The Santa
Monica house offered at first and withdrawn after he
found out that she was not the mouse he thought, so
that Locke went to Hollywood alone after all. Eric,
late at the airport so that she had to deal with the press
alone, hinting that Locke had arranged for Mort to
advise her on her appearance. Eric forgetting to tell
her to dress for a pool party, Eric disputing the facts
about Sandy and Locke in a dressing room, yet
encouraging the conversation he knew she must
overhear.

Dru stared at the golden shell in her hand. At least
she knew *that* was the truth. Eric might have made
sure she overheard all about Sandy but he wasn't
fabricating the story. Locke himself had corroborated
that with his evasions over the 'phone calls.

'It's a Golden Cowrie,' Locke said behind her and
she swung around, startled. 'Van collects shells and all
these other things——' he gestured at the shelves,
then took the Cowrie from her to put it back. 'Dru,' he
said taking her hands, 'I'm sorry about Sandy. When
she kept 'phoning the apartment I meant to tell you
but you assumed it was a man and I let you because—
well, because I didn't want to have to explain. You're
always so sarcastic about my . . .'

'Women?' she pulled her hands free.

'It was over between us before I met you.'

'Judging by the 'phone calls she doesn't know that.'

'She knew. We did have a brief . . .'

'Affair?'

He took her shoulders in an angry grip. 'It's over,

just in case you're imagining otherwise. Finished. Sandy is spoiled rotten and doesn't like to give up her——'

'Playthings?'

He shook her. 'I swear, Dru, I'll put you over my knee again if you keep this up. I didn't lie to you, I merely let you make your own assumptions that Sandy was a man.'

He really wanted to convince her. Locke must want to hang on to his new domestic image. A divorce too soon would turn him right back into the Ransome Man.

'I made another assumption too and I'll bet I'm right about this one. I assume that Sandy was the "old friend" you stayed on to see in Melbourne.'

He stared at her. 'What?'

'Harve Randall mentioned you and your old friend in his column three days ago. Quite a coincidence that you were in Melbourne at the same time, he said.'

'But he didn't mention the friend's name,' Locke said slowly.

'Lucky weren't you?'

'I stayed on to see Hal Spencer,' he said sharply. 'We were at NIDA together. Hal's been looking for a break and I happened to know that the *Ramage* producers had considered him for my part originally. Eric had the negotiations practically concluded when I decided I definitely didn't want *Ramage* again in a big way. I ran into Hal and wondered if I couldn't turn my refusal to his benefit. I owed him a favour.' He paused. 'The show format is too popular to discard— after Eric came back here I put the proposition to them that I would contract to do several guest spots in the series if they found themselves another Ramage. It's a long shot but I was going to turn it down anyway and it might do Hal some good. Eric was upset of course, but he understood when I explained how I felt.'

She doubted that. 'So you weren't with Sandy——?'

'Until tonight I hadn't seen her since March.' His hands slipped down from her shoulders to grip her arms. 'Now you tell me something. If you were making assumptions about her being with me in Melbourne days ago, you had obviously already heard about her. Tonight was not the revelation I had thought. So when did you find out?'

His green eyes were extraordinarily intent.

'On the opening night of *Man Alive*——' she felt his fingers tighten. There was a sudden glitter in his eyes, 'I overheard Melanie say you'd married me as a smokescreen for your lovelife and especially for your affair with Sandy and because you'd had those 'phone calls, I thought she was right——'

'Melanie's a stupid woman. And I'm an idiot.' He curved a hand to her head. 'Opening night—was that why our celebration turned out a fiasco, Dru? We were doing just fine until then. Was a bit of malicious gossip responsible for your crack about the play? And for refusing me?' His head bent, he nuzzled his way across her cheek until his lips were touching hers— 'Was that why you let me think it was *him* still——? Her lips moved to answer him but the words were lost in a kiss that went on and on . . . 'That champagne—is it still on ice?' he said huskily in her ear.

'Okay, okay, break it up you two,' Eric laughed from the doorway. 'I can't have my star guest sneaking off to neck with his wife even if he is my brother.'

'In that case, we'd better leave,' Locke said.

Both Van and Eric saw them out. Eric gave Locke the latest publicity file of press clippings. 'See if there's anyone you want to sue this month,' he joked. 'Hey, we're going up to the reef for a few days soon. Why don't you come?'

'Not this time,' Locke tucked the file under his arm and smiled down at Dru, 'We might sneak away alone though for a weekend. We never did finish the painting at Sea Winds.'

'Did you enjoy your weekend up there, Dru? Was it warm enough to swim in September?' Vanessa asked.

Dru looked blankly at the girl. How had she known about her trip away? Locke's arm stiffened at her waist. She became aware that her surprised silence might look like guilt.

'The sea wasn't exactly warm. I would have told you I went up,' she said to Locke, 'but you made such a fuss at the idea of me staying at the beach alone.'

'You chauvinist, Locke,' Van accused.

'You can't play the heavy husband these days, old son. Women won't stand for it. And anyway who says she was alone?' Eric winked roguishly. 'You won't mind me saying it pet, but in the old days you looked like a girl who'd spend her time alone but now——' he leaned back, hands spread wide and admired her new look, 'Rah, rah, rah. I'll bet you just couldn't wait to go back and show them all what they missed out on. Michael for instance, eh?'

Locke's face froze up.

'Oh look——' Eric was all concern. 'It was a joke . . .'

'Come on, Locke, just because Dru went away without telling you doesn't mean . . .' Van began.

'For God's sake, Van,' Eric hissed. 'Be quiet.'

It was artistic. Convincing. They had put their foot in it quite by accident or so it would appear to Locke. Dru didn't believe it for a moment.

'A weekend away and you just forgot to mention it,' Locke sneered when they were in the car.

'I didn't forget. I just didn't want to get into another argument about my being there alone.'

'If you *were* alone,' he said roughly. 'And I've never noticed any reluctance on your part to get involved in arguments.'

'Of course I was alone—don't swallow Eric's nicely planted——' she backtracked on that fast. Now was not the time to tell him that Eric was trying to break them up. She had no proof—Eric had never done or said anything in front of Locke except to elaborately defend her. Even that had been designed to make her look unsuitable, but it was all a matter of interpretation. There wasn't Dru realised dismally, a single thing she could point to that would ring true. She would merely sound neurotic, Eric would come up smelling like a rose and Locke would hate her for it. Besides, even if she could prove his interference, how was she going to hurt Locke with it? Her mind raced. If she could just hold on, Eric would slip up and Locke would find out for himself—that would be by far the best way ... 'I went to see Barry and Jan. Then I saw Gillian and hired a car and drove to the beach,' she said in a matter-of-fact voice. 'I re-painted the Sea Winds sign and—and tidied up a bit in Sam's place. I know that probably sounds stupid, but I dusted his things and swept the floor ...'

He parked the Rover and they took the elevator. Inside the apartment, Locke tossed the publicity file on to the marble coffee table, and put his hands on his hips.

'Is it still Pennington? Did I assume too much tonight, thinking it was just jealousy about Sandy that made you reject me on opening night? Is he the reason you were reluctant to come to Hollywood with me—so that you could pretty yourself and fly up to see him?'

'What do you mean, reluctant? I wanted to go—but when Eric wouldn't—couldn't—let us have his house, you said staying in a hotel was no good. And I thought you and Eric had decided I was too much of a risk after what I said about the play.'

Eric, she thought. You might be asking a lot of Dru,

old son, he'd probably said to Locke. She's worried sick about mixing it with the Hollywood set but doesn't like to say. Feels she might be letting you down. Better give her more time.

'If I gave you any impression of reluctance—it was because I was jealous of Sandy—thinking of you seeing her after those late, late rehearsals and performances.'

'Hmmph. I keep forgetting that you had that fiction on your mind.' He walked over to her, shoving his hands into his pockets. 'You had plenty of reason to believe it I guess—what with my reputation and the nature of our marriage.' He came and stood close to her and Dru's heartbeat accelerated. 'I'm jealous too, Dru,' he said softly. 'But I know that I only have to be afraid of a man you love. You aren't the kind to experiment for kicks.' He took her by the shoulders, 'So tell me you haven't seen Pennington and I can stop acting like a fool.'

'Locke, about Michael—I don't——' love him, she wanted to say. But his grip increased and he pulled her fractionally closer.

'Tell me,' he urged and there was a warmth and promise in his eyes that needed only a simple 'no' for release. She thought of that boring lunch with Michael at his hotel—a totally meaningless thing and weighed it against this new beginning. Later, when she had had the night to show him how much she loved him—later she could tell him what a joke that lunch had been ... Dru put her arms around his neck.

'No—I didn't see Michael, and I don't want to,' she whispered and she did what she had promised herself on the play's first night. She kissed him.

Locke was surprised. Her lips moved on his, her tongue flicked at him and she leaned back to smile at his bemused expression. He touched her face, moved his hand to accommodate the curve of her jaw. There was a look in his eyes that awed her, delighted her. She felt beautiful.

'You know, it's time we had that celebration,' he murmured.

'I won't argue with that. The champagne has been on ice long enough. And so have I——'

He bent his head and kissed her neck, inching his way to her ear. 'Let's take this nice and easy——' he said softly, '. . . why don't you——'

'Slip into something comfortable?' she giggled. There was the sound of nerves in it. Locke held her close and stroked her hair.

'Nice and easy,' he repeated in reassurance. 'I want to tell you . . .' He stopped and laughed, put her away from him, 'No—go and change. I'll propose a toast in a little while.' He went to his bedroom, she went to hers. The last time they would do that, Dru thought as she threw off her designer dress and tossed it on the floor. She showered, stroked on *L'Air du Temps* in daring places. The silk nightdress dropped over her head with a sensuous slither. Dru smiled as she tied the two sets of ribbons that closed the deep slashed front together at just two points. Soon Locke would untie them again . . .

He was waiting in the lounge room. An ice bucket was on the marble slab coffee table with the unopened bottle in it. Two glasses stood beside it. Locke had his back to her. His hair was damp, his feet were bare. He wore a short robe tied at the waist. Dru stood there, marvelling at him. His legs were long and muscular and the hair on them darkened as if he had not dried them entirely. The robe clung to his buttocks and narrow hips, pulled across the flaring width of his back and shoulders.

'I wondered what you would wear,' she said inanely and heard her voice emerge too high. 'On opening night, I tossed up between those indecent pyjama trousers, a brocade dressing gown—or . . .' He turned and she saw his eyes. '. . . nothing.'

All the warmth had died. Locke's mouth was hard, his jaw set. As he turned all the way around she saw that he held Eric's publicity file in his hands.

'So you didn't see Pennington,' he said and tossed the file on to a chair near her. Dru went to look at it, turning the pages until she saw it. 'Elegant Dru Matthews, wife of screen star Locke Matthews and daughter of former Olympic swimmer Wes Winters, lunching with Michael Pennington at his hotel recently . . .' She closed her eyes. What timing.

'Locke, I was going to tell you tomorrow. It didn't mean anything—I was sure you were in Melbourne with Sandy at the time.'

'You arranged it while you were up at the beach I suppose? Where you assured me you hadn't seen him.'

'I didn't. He wrote to me at Gillian's address. She gave me the letter and I had no intention of accepting his invitation at first . . .'

'And you were going to tell me—now isn't that nice? I suppose you were going to tell me about taking off for the weekend too. How many other things might I discover that you haven't yet mentioned?'

Dru felt cold. The magic had slipped away again.

'It's mutual then isn't it, Locke? You didn't even tell me I was to be your second wife—you didn't bother to enlighten me as to Sandy's gender.'

'We've been through that,' he said dismissively with an arrogant, scissor movement of his hands. 'But you and Pennington! Couldn't you resist it, Dru? Showing him what he threw away? The new *elegant* Dru Matthews—did he come running, Dru, to admire you now that you've acquired the glamour of being married to me?'

That stung. As if she had no individuality of her own.

'Naturally,' she snapped. 'Any woman chosen by the great Lothario himself has to be reconsidered as an asset—out of bed and in.'

He grabbed her arm and yanked her to him. 'Eric's right. You've changed.'

Dru's frustration boiled over at his brother's name.

'Maybe you should think twice about what Eric says. If it hadn't been for him, we'd be drinking champagne and—and making love by now.'

'Eric?' Locke repeated. She might as well have told him that the Martians had landed. 'What the hell has any of this to do with Eric?'

'Everything,' she cried, driven by those fading images of him tenderly holding her through the night, 'He produced Sandy tonight to humiliate me and come between us, but it backfired. Instead, we reached an understanding but Eric doesn't want that. So he dropped his little bombshell about my weekend away, or got Van to drop it for him—and I'll bet it's no accident that he gave you that file just then—clever of him not to even mention the picture of me, as if he assumed you'd know all about my lunch date with another man—of course he couldn't know just what fantastic timing it was but . . .' she stopped. Locke was looking at her as if she was demented. Inwardly she groaned. It would sound like ravings to him. Why hadn't she kept quiet about it? 'He—he has been trying to break us up, Locke,' she felt compelled to go on now that she'd started and heard herself babbling again as she took his arm. 'If it hadn't been for Eric I wouldn't have overheard Melanie talking about you and Sandy—he tried to make me feel an outsider—and it was Eric who didn't want us to go to Hollywood together. When you came back he made me think you had been ashamed of me and asked Mort to give me a few tips——'

Locke threw off her grip and stepped back.

'My God,' he shook his head, 'You ungrateful little

bitch. He's done his best to help you fit in—invited you to a party while I was away, introduced you around—even took your side when you criticised the play——' he walked around her, viewing her in the bridal nightgown as if she was something new in his experience. 'I wouldn't have believed it—even the photograph of you and Pennington didn't really convince me that you'd done any more than lied to me about seeing him. But to clutch at straws like this— actually trying to lay blame on *Eric*, of all people! My brother—and a friend who got me through the worst times of my life, who has worked his butt off to make me successful. You have to be hiding more than lies to try a diversion on that scale, Dru . . .'

He came to a stop in front of her, reached out to the ties of her gown. The silk ribbons untied at a touch. She held his wrists but it made no difference. Locke pushed aside the edges of her gown, touched her breasts and stroked a finger down her midriff to her navel. At her quick, indrawn breath he raised his eyes to her face.

'Less than ten minutes ago I wanted you so much it was a pain in my gut,' he said harshly. With a jerk he closed her gown, re-tied the top ribbons. 'Now I think I'll have a scotch instead.'

After that he was a virtual stranger to her. But sometimes Dru felt his eyes on her and once she saw uncertainty on his face. Knowing her as he did, he must surely find it difficult to believe that she would cheat. But her own idiocy and Eric's prompting had laid too many doubts. Dru took some small comforts with her through the following days. Locke had wanted her. And the old affection had been there for her during that brief ceasefire between Eric's bombshells. There was a marriage to be made if they were left alone to make it. In the end she did the only thing she could. She went to see Eric.

A decorative secretary—blonde of course—showed her through to his office. Eric's desk was a mite smaller than an average swimming pool. An exquisite sculpture stood on it and an oriental arrangement of lilies, driftwood and smooth river stones which looked like Vanessa's work. A run of cabinets and a cocktail bar filled two walls. Enlarged movie stills of Locke filled another. Eric's head, with its thinning red hair was outlined in cruel contrast against the pictures.

'Hello, pet.' he said without any of the usual razzamatazz that accompanied his greetings. But then, she thought—it had been a while since Eric had given her the full treatment. He must have decided to get rid of her when he stopped kissing her hello and goodbye.

'I know what you're doing, Eric,' she said evenly.

'You finally caught on. I thought you might when I produced Sandy.'

She felt a jab of alarm. He wasn't even going to deny it. 'Locke wouldn't like what's happening.'

He smiled. 'I'd be careful about telling tales to him pet—he wouldn't be crazy about anyone who besmirched his big brother's name——' His smile grew at Dru's quick swallow, 'Ah—I see you've already discovered that. Silly girl.' He shook his head. 'What did you say about me? Naughty Eric tried to embarrass me at his parties? Dropped a few hints on fertile ground? There's not much to go on, is there pet?'

'So you admit you tried to humiliate me.'

'Sure. Our crowd can be pretty overpowering. I figured it wouldn't take too much exposure to it to make you run. At first I didn't think you were going to be any trouble. If you'd stayed in the background pet, kept quiet like at the wedding and hadn't started putting ideas into Locke's head then maybe I could have lived with it.'

Dru had a chilling sensation up her spine. 'But you

found out that I could take care of myself among your bitchy, patronising friends, didn't you?'

Anger flashed across his face snarling his features briefly. 'It was disappointing,' he admitted and picked up a pen, turned it over and over, watching it, 'But you'll go. In the end.'

His quiet confidence made her shiver. Someone waiting, Philomena had said. But not in the dark anymore.

'I won't,' she told him. 'Philomena was right—I hold on to what I want.'

He hooted. 'That old cow! What would she know?'

'She knows what I know, Eric. I won't leave Locke.'

'You will. You never belonged with him in the first case. I tried to tell him but sometimes he's stubborn as a mule. I couldn't believe it when I saw you. That he would choose *you* of all women! He even told me later that you still hankered after an old boyfriend. The fool doesn't even have the conceit to realise that women forget other men for him. Oh you love him all right,' he smiled, 'As I told him. The same way I told you that he and Sandy weren't lovers anymore. Funny how the truth sounds phony if you just say it earnestly enough. Of course,' Eric went on twirling the pen, 'he didn't mention the boyfriend's name. But you said something about a Michael and then—what do you know—I come across a picture of Dru having lunch with Michael. It was a nice touch don't you think— tossing his name in alongside the news of your weekend away? I knew you hadn't told Locke you'd gone from something he said. Your reticence and the lunch date must have made your weekend look so illicit to him, pet.'

'I suppose someone saw me at the airport?'

'One of my friends.'

'Have you got any?'

'Tch, tch. Don't get abusive, Dru.'

She made a conscious effort to calm herself. There was something here, something she wasn't reaching. Her gaze went to the stills behind him. One was from a *Ramage* episode. She recognised the car used in the series. A *red* sports car ... a Porsche. She'd forgotten that Ramage had raced around in one. As Eric did now. The image of his sports car in her rear vision mirror had bothered her that day. An early evening ...

'I think Hal Spencer will make a great Ramage,' she said, testing for reaction. Eric erupted from his swivel chair. His face was a study in fury and frustration.

'No one else can do it. Locke *is* Ramage.'

'Was.'

'I have you to thank for that,' he spat. 'You and your suburban little mind. "You know I don't personally like the show"'—he mimicked her voice, 'I was so *sure* he would sign. He let me think he would and talked me into coming back. He tricked me to do a favour for a friend——' He looked desolate and Dru felt sorry for him until he turned on her with a snarl, 'It was your fault. He would never have thought of giving up the series but for you.'

'Locke makes his own decisions. He was ready for change before he met me.'

'No.'

'He'll never make any more *Ramage* anyway,' she prodded. She had to step back from the desk. Eric's glare across it was almost a physical blow. This was it, she thought sickly. The something she knew was there. It had been staring her in the face. 'No more *Ramage* and no more *Ransome Man*, Eric. Not for Locke. And not for you.'

He clenched his fists. 'I created it—I created him, and I'm not going to let you ruin years of work.'

'*You* are the Ransome Man, aren't you, Eric? You

created the image and your brother gives it form on the screen, but you live it all the time. That's why you can't stand the thought of Locke turning to more serious work. Apart from the money you need the image. But for Locke it was never real and he's tired of it. Give up, Eric—removing me won't make any difference now. And anyway, I won't go.'

'You'll go if Locke wants you to,' Eric said and smirked at her reaction. 'I can see now I'll have to work on him instead of you.'

'He's your brother!' she exclaimed, sick to the heart. 'How can you say that?'

'It's for the best. Locke knows I've always done everything with his best interests in mind. Ever since we were kids.'

Ever since you grew up ordinary and he grew up sensational and your girlfriends found your kid brother more interesting. Dru felt terribly sorry for Eric. By accident he had stumbled on a way of dealing with his inadequacies—to advertise a client's product he had designed the fantasy man he would like to be— that thousands of men would like to be—and somehow all that he must have envied in his kid brother had found their way into the creation. No wonder Locke had won the *Ransome* job. The role had been written for him.

'I could tell Locke about this conversation,' she said.

'He wouldn't believe it,' Eric smiled. 'He really wouldn't pet.'

'How do you know I haven't got a tape recorder in my bag?' Dru backed away as he shot towards her. But he was fast. He caught her against his filing drawers and snatched her bag from her shoulder. The contents scattered over the carpet and Eric shook out the bag and gave it back to her.

'Sorry about that pet,' he said and the conversational

tone frightened her more than those few seconds of near violence—'But I had to be sure.'

He went back to his desk while she picked up the contents of her handbag with trembling fingers.

'Mum is coming to visit soon,' Eric told her as if nothing untoward had occurred. 'She usually spends a few days with Locke and few with me. So I guess we'll be seeing you for a family dinner sometime after Van and I come back from the reef.'

As she left, his secretary was re-applying lipstick in the outer office. But for one of his dumb blondes, Locke would never have gone to Sea Winds. It had a sad sort of irony.

Dru felt cold for a long time afterwards. Eric was sick. He needed help. But how could she tell Locke so, having already earned his contempt with what seemed like petty accusations of his brother? Eric would preserve his usual bonhomie in front of Locke and others, he would quietly lay his poison against her and she could do nothing about it. Dru considered broaching the subject with Irene when she came. But then, how to tell a mother that her son had succumbed to the fantasy world he had created to advertise razors? It sounded like the product of a hysterical mind. There seemed nothing she could do but wait and hope that Eric might give himself away. Meanwhile the odd marriage which had come so close to the genuine thing was reeling to a standstill. She avoided her brother-in-law, refusing to remain in the apartment when he called by.

'Hello pet,' Eric would say, all smiles and her forced answer and quick getaway would intensify the frown that always sat on Locke's brow of late. The combination of his suspicion about Michael and her antipathy to his brother was killing the affection Locke had for her. Once he asked her if she wanted to call it quits. When she said no, he smiled cynically. 'There wouldn't be much alimony in it just yet, would there?' he said, referring to the brevity of the marriage.

Dru nearly spilled out her misery to Gillian whose flying schedule found her in Sydney one day. But their lunch together was to be short and the story so long that she decided against it. Gillian was still dieting, still dating a 'way-out' man (new) and still as disinterested in Sea Winds as ever. Barry had had an offer for the holiday house, she said, and wasn't it time they got rid of it?

'Barry doesn't want to sell, the spoilsport—because he heard some rumour that one of the services clubs might drain that swamp and build a casino near us. But you know there has been talk of draining it for years and nothing ever happens. If you say sell, Barry will be outvoted,' she said hopefully.

'Who made the offer?'

'Oh who knows—some company I've never heard of—say you'll sell out, Dru . . .'

Dru shook her head and Gillian groaned. 'There goes my Hamilton townhouse.'

Barry was pleased though when he 'phoned the next day and found that Dru agreed with him.

'If that project comes up, Dru, old Sea Winds or rather the land she stands on, might be worth a small fortune. Far better to hang on to it for a while longer.'

Dru was depressed. She didn't want to hold on to the holiday house for speculation—but simply because she was fond of it. Gloomily she realised that the rumours about the project were probably right. Two offers—one for Sea Winds and the one for Sam's place indicated a sudden interest in the stretch of beachfront which couldn't just be coincidence. When and if that swamp was drained, she would be outvoted and Sea Winds would be sold. Gillian would use her share of the sale price for her townhouse, Barry would no doubt plough his into his business and she—she would have a cold sum of money listed in a bank account. And Sea Winds, with its ramshackle shed and its dark stairs that held memories of childhood fears and of meeting Locke, would be gone.

Eric and Van went north to the reef. Dru wished they were going for several weeks instead of just a few days. Who knows, she thought uncharitably, an early cyclone might blow them out to sea in their game fishing boat—wash them up on a desert island somewhere in the Pacific where they could do no more harm. Van would like that—no busty blondes to compete for Eric's attention. The idea of Eric minus his three-piece suits, manicures, French champagne and celebrities cheered her. Just for a little while anyway.

CHAPTER TEN

DRU was alone the night she took a call from the property agent. Just an hour ago, he said—Sam's place had burned down. Probably the work of kids, he said. It was deliberately set and went up like tinder. By the time the fire brigade got there it had collapsed. Lucky it hadn't been a nice, new place—he said. Lucky it was just an old shack with nothing of value in it—he said. Dru hung up. Lucky. She walked to the window and looked out at the black, city-speckled night. Sam's cottage, narrow and patch-painted with its illusion of a lean to one side just like Sam himself. When she went to Sea Winds again, there would be nothing of him left. She was crying when Locke came home. When she gulped out the news he took her in his arms for the first time since the night of Eric's party.

'I'm sorry, Dru—I know how you feel——'

'All his worthless things—I wish I'd taken them but somehow they belonged there. I meant to take the dragon and I forgot. How could I have forgotten?'

He soothed her and through her distress for this last parting from Sam she felt his warmth and took strength from it. In spite of Eric and Eva, Locke still loved her a little.

They put on a show for Irene when she came to stay. And in the acting, some of their pretend smiles became the genuine thing and the atmosphere lifted. Dru moved out of her room and into Locke's to accommodate his mother.

It was odd, awkward to share with him. There was intimacy in the sight of her clothes with his in the wall-side wardrobe, her hairbrush and his side by side.

Her pillow and his. He came in while she was undressing the first night and misreading her startled look said:

'Don't worry—I won't touch you. You'll sleep in peace tonight—the way you told me you always do.'

He stayed up long after Dru went to bed and he made no move towards her when he came in. Later when he cried out in his sleep, she turned to him and put her arms around him. This time he didn't say Eva's name, but the pain was there. He held on to her in his sleep as if he needed her. He didn't wake. She wasn't sure if that was a good or a bad thing.

In the morning he went out early.

'Fencing lessons,' he told Irene when she asked where he was going.

'Good lord Lachlan—are you thinking of doing a swashbuckler?'

He grinned. 'Who knows? This is theatrical fencing—all choreographed. It's good for the reflexes and could come in handy some time.'

'He had that old nightmare again last night,' Irene commented when he'd left.

'You heard?'

'Well I heard him call out "no, no" and I didn't think he was fighting off your advances dear,' she joked then at Dru's expression added. 'You know about Eva I suppose?'

'Not much. Was she pretty?'

'Oh yes. Pretty and vivacious——' she studied Dru and shook her head. 'No my dear, it isn't what you think. If he dreams of Eva it is because of the manner of her death, not because he hasn't stopped mourning her. Oh, he loved her. Very much. He was twenty-four—she was twenty-one. They hadn't a bean between them but they were happy. Lachlan arranged to meet her in town one day after she finished work. His audition had dragged on and he was running late.

When he got near the street corner where they'd agreed to meet, there was an overturned truck and the police and a crowd of onlookers. He went past it to look for Eva, thinking she might be in one of the shops, bored with waiting for him. When he heard the police talking about trying to release a pedestrian from the wreckage . . .'

'Oh no,' Dru put her hands to her face, 'No——'

'. . . he didn't—*wouldn't* believe it could be Eva. One of the police asked him if his wife was wearing a pink dress and he even swore that Eva didn't have one.'

She never wears pink, he'd cried that very first time at Sea Winds. A frantic denial of the colour that might identify his young wife. He wouldn't let the saleswoman show her a pink dress, she remembered now. And he'd berated her for keeping him waiting— imagining perhaps another accident on another street corner.

'The dream hasn't bothered him for a long time but now——' she hesitated, looking at Dru, '——he seems to have reached some crisis point and who knows what makes his mind look backwards. A little guilt I suppose—if he'd been on time he used to say, she might not have died—or a fear of loss again now that he has someone he loves at last.'

Someone he loves, Dru thought. She would like to believe that.

'. . . nice girls don't abound in the life of a man like Lachlan. Certainly not since he became famous anyway. Nice, normal girls don't want to get to know a man in the glare of publicity. I thank God for that two weeks he had at the beach with you . . . you were able to see him for what he was—and he could find out what he was missing . . .'

If that were so, then he might be missing it again soon if Eric had his way. Tonight she would have to smile and be as charmingly insincere as Eric himself in order to keep peace with Locke and Irene. For Eric was back from his big-game fishing and had insisted on having a 'family dinner' at his house.

Locke arrived home that afternoon, carrying flowers.

'Just like his father,' Irene said to Dru, 'Whenever Johnny stayed out drinking with his friends he brought flowers to smooth his way. So don't you try to tell us that you spent all day fencing, Lachlan.'

'Egad, Madam,' he plucked a gladioli spike from the flowers and tossed the fragrant sheaf to Dru. 'Will you scold a man for slaking his thirst? Take care . . .' he advanced on Irene, one hand on hip, the other parrying an imaginary rapier with the drooping gladioli. 'Aha!' he did a Fairbanks laugh as he tickled Irene's ear with the flower. 'Will you surrender, Madam?' She laughed as he hugged her.

'Oh Lachlan, I'd love to see you do a swashbuckler— don't you think he'd be superb, Dru?'

'A natural I should think. He could grow a beard— wouldn't have to shave for months.'

He felt his chin. 'Ah, Madam landlady,' he grinned and it was the way it used to be with them. Whatever he had been drinking had relaxed the stern control he'd exercised the past weeks.

Later he came into the bathroom just as Dru was pulling her dress over her head. At the sound of his approach she had rushed and forgotten the hook. His soft laugh reached her through the fabric folds over her head.

'Let me help,' he said. She couldn't see him but felt his fingers touch her neck, release the hook then pull the garment upwards so that her arms raised high in the air.

'Thanks.' She made a snatch at the dress but he tossed it aside and grinned at her bra and briefed figure. Alcohol had put a lazy, sexy light in his eyes. He looked fantastic in a figure hugging cotton tee shirt and jeans.

'Do you mind, Locke, I'm about to take a shower.'

He shook his head, leaned a shoulder on the wall in a familiar pose. 'I don't mind one bit. Want some help?'

She reddened. 'Sssh. Your mother's next door.'

'Is that your only objection?'

Dru grabbed at a towel but he moved and cut her off.

'You're drunk.'

His eyes bleakened. 'No such luck.' He reached for her, wrapped his arms about her near naked body and bent his head so that it rested in the hollow of her shoulder. On a long, shuddering sigh, he raked a hand into her cropped hair and turned her face upwards. His kiss was awkward, uncontrolled. Over her back his hands slid and pressed in seeming uncertainty. This was not the experienced lover, but an inarticulate boy trying to tell her something . . . Dru returned his kiss, held him close, wishing that this was not whisky inspired.

'I'm sorry,' he muttered as he released her. 'I did promise I wouldn't touch you didn't I? I thought I didn't even want to——'

'Locke, I don't love Michael—I don't care a damn about him,' she blurted out.

'Sure.' He sounded weary now. And sober. Taking his towel he went to the door.

'I don't love him you big oaf——' she insisted, wanting to shout but remembering his mother. 'I love you.'

But the door had already closed.

He showered in the other bathroom then slept off his afternoon drinks. By the time they left for the 'family dinner' at Eric's house, Locke was cool and distant again.

Eric and Van were model hosts. Well, Eric was at least. Vanessa seemed a bit on edge. In a way, Dru felt sorry for her even if she had played her part in Eric's schemes. She probably loved him and her chances of enjoying a permanent relationship with him were slim. Maybe she had already been given her marching orders, Dru thought, eyeing Vanessa's half hearted efforts to eat.

'That buyer still wants your beachfront. He's upped the price old son,' Eric winked at Locke, 'You'd do well to think about it.'

Dru frowned. How very persistent Eric was about Sam's land, she thought. Just who was this anxious buyer of his . . . someone who had heard the rumours about the building project—maybe the same buyer who had made an offer for Sea Winds? Maybe Eric himself had heard them . . . Eric who had the expenses of a star and a gambler. He'd sold things Mrs Curtis said. The ruby ring hadn't been around for a while and come to think of it one of his paintings wasn't in its place. Dru tried to remember just what she had said to him when he first began talking about selling. The exact words escaped her . . .

'Say—that's bad luck,' Eric was saying to Locke, 'The old guy's shack! But the agent did say it was a fire trap. It must have been a shock for you, Dru. I know how much it meant to you.' And he couldn't care less. His phony sympathy grated on her.

'If you think I'll agree to sell now, forget it,' she said rudely. 'And don't count on getting Locke to talk me into it.'

Irene looked aghast at her. Locke frowned. Vanessa looked edgier than ever.

'Pet——' Eric was reproachful, 'You mustn't take it so personally. I handle Locke's financial affairs and it would be unprofessional of me not to put him wise to a good offer like this.'

'*Us*,' she snapped and knew she was sounding petulant. 'This piece of property is jointly owned. And I think it might be better off under our own management.'

'For God's sake, Dru!' Locke exclaimed. Irene murmured something, then made a concerted effort to change the subject which stayed changed until Eric's domestic help removed the dessert dishes from the table. It was Irene's suggestion that they look at Eric's art collection. They wandered through to the pool so that she could view a sculpture there, then followed Vanessa. Dru trailed behind—an outcast. For the first time she was even sensing disapproval from Irene.

'We bought a super wall-hanging near Cairns. From an artists' commune,' Van said as they went into the sun room with its lacquered oriental furniture and the glass shelves full of amethyst deposits and sea-shells. The wall-hanging was an artistic, ragged weaving of jute and natural dyed wools. Dru never looked at it after a first fleeting glimpse. She stared at the glass shelves and remembered just what she had said when Eric first suggested selling Sam's place. 'That pile of junk belonged to a friend and whilever it stands, the land will remain as he wanted it.'

Whilever it stands.

On one of the glass shelves stood the driftwood dragon.

Tears came and she brushed them away, trying to clear her mind. This was important, too important to be risked by emotion. Isn't that right, Sam?

The others turned away from the wall-hanging.

'Where did you get this?' Dru asked Vanessa, her voice husky. Locke glanced at her, frowned and followed her gaze.

'Oh—I, er picked it up while we were in the north—

it's nice isn't it?' Van said, 'Have you seen my Wentletrap—they're really quite rare shells . . .'

Dru didn't look at the Wentletrap Van held out.

'It's one of Sam's carvings,' she said and turned slowly to look at Locke. 'The dragon. I meant to bring it away with me last time I was up there and I—I forgot. It should have burned in the fire . . .'

'It's just a piece of driftwood pet,' Eric said as if he was being tolerant over some new childishness, 'But you can have it if it reminds you of the old man.'

He didn't know, Dru realised. Eric didn't know that Vanessa had given them away by picking up a piece of timber.

'It has my name on it,' she said almost reluctantly, feeling sorry for Eric now and even sorrier for Locke as he picked up the driftwood and turned it over.

'Silla——' his thumb moved over the letters. 'But how . . .' he began.

'Oh, I noticed it had letters on it when I picked it up,' Vanessa said brightly, too brightly. 'But it isn't your name.'

'My name is Drusilla. Sam always called me Silla.'
Dead silence.

'I didn't know Silla was anyone's name,' Van said in a high voice. 'I wouldn't have taken it if I'd known . . .'

Eric turned on her. 'You stupid bitch—haven't you got enough stuff here without picking up another bit of rubbish?'

'It was beautiful and I couldn't resist——' her composure fell apart. 'Oh God, Eric, we should never have done it—I told you we shouldn't——'

'Shut up!'

'Did what?' Irene demanded. 'And kindly don't use language like that, Eric——'

'What did she mean, Eric?' Locke asked. 'Were you and Van in Sam's place? What shouldn't you have done?' His face was drawn, austere.

'Look old son, I can explain everything.' Eric said the classic line with a desperate smile that made Dru feel sick. 'It wasn't worth anything—it was a pile of junk—I did everyone a favour getting rid of it . . .'

Dru started to turn away, unable to bear the cornered look on Eric's face and the beginning of pain on Locke's. Her movement seemed to snap everything in Eric.

'I'm glad I destroyed it,' he snarled, 'It was something you loved and that made it a double pleasure to burn. You've spoiled everything haven't you pet—you shouldn't have met him. You were never supposed to be in his life . . .' He made a threatening move towards Dru. Locke restrained him. Vanessa clung to Eric's arm.

'I'm sorry——' she cried, 'I should have done something sooner but I didn't want to lose him——'

Irene sat down suddenly on one of the settees.

'Leave us, Dru,' Locke said tersely. And she went, tears streaming down her face.

There were no footmarks on the beach. It was early, very early morning and a haze marked the horizon. October was not so different from April here. The days began chilly and warmed by mid-morning to a delicious heat that lacked the sting of full summer. Gulls shrieked and circled over the unmarked sand.

Dru stood at her curtainless bedroom window and let her eyes drift to that charred patch among the singed cotton trees. This was her third day here, and now she could look at the remains of Sam's house without the choking emotion of the first and the desolation of the second. The gulls tightened into a hungry group. Their cries grew sharper, more plaintive. As Dru watched, a boy of maybe twelve hove into view, leaning with the weight of a fishing basket and bait bucket. He stopped and tossed out something. The gulls dropped from the sky to quarrel over their breakfast and the boy walked on, his fishing rod quivering, leaving his footprints behind. Things changed, Sam had said.

His dragon sat beside her bed. Dru bent to pick it up. Dear Sam. She rememberd the day she'd first seen him carving it. The shush of surf and gulls cries. His delicate work had rung down the curtain on Eric's pretences. If she had taken it away with her that weekend, how long might it have been before Eric was exposed? But something had stopped her. Something.

I'd like to see you happy, Silla, Sam had said. She moved the dragon and it lost form, became the simple, striking piece of timber that Vanessa had thought would never be recognised. She might never even have seen the elusive dragon—just a beautiful shape.

Neither Locke nor his mother had come home that dreadful night. Irene arrived by cab later in the morning. She was grey and weary—all the optimisitic lines of her face dragged downwards. As she packed a bag for Locke she confirmed that they had the whole story. She cried much of it out on Dru's shoulder.

'He'll have to have treatment, Dru—Locke is seeing to it. He's so patient, so understanding after all that Eric's done to him. Eric was short of money because he'd run up so many gambling debts and the U.S. Revenue people are after him for back taxes—he found out that there was some building project planned near your beach property and wanted to get you to sell to him. His buyer was actually himself—he'd set up a company name just for that—when the new building was announced officially he could have re-sold at a huge profit—oh my dear, I'm sorry about your friend's house . . .' She cried some more.

Eric had meddled with other investments because of his financial pressures. He'd always thought he could put them all right again with Locke's next film. Eric was caught in a vicious circle. He had to keep up his image—he had to have money because that was part of the Ransome image—and both those things were in Locke's control. Dru had come along just when everything was about to change anyway. Eric saw his little world coming to an end but he couldn't do anything about it. So he crystallised all his problems and made Dru responsible for them. It was her fault he convinced himself that Locke was rocking the boat. Everything had been okay before she came and would be when she went away again. Poor deluded Eric.

A cab took the bag to Locke. He wouldn't come home, Irene said until he had sorted out things for his brother. Together he and Vanessa would arrange matters so that the press were kept out of it for as long as possible. Then there were the financial problems to combat. Locke would have to go to Melbourne and the States to establish the extent of Eric's debts and iron out any negotiations in progress. Dru longed to be with Locke, hold him—offer the comfort he must need right now. But she was symbolic of all Eric's losses and had to stay away or risk making matters worse.

Three days she waited in the apartment, hoping for a 'phone call from Locke. But—nothing. Irene stayed with her, but nodded her understanding when Dru said she had to get away and do something to fill the days of waiting. Irene too, was anxious to return to the comforting surroundings of her own home to await news of Eric. Before she left, she put a letter on Locke's desk. 'The boy might need a few encouraging words when he gets back,' she said.

Dru had left a letter too. A very short letter. He might not have been home to read it yet. She put down the dragon and began to dress in her painting clothes. She painted two upstairs window frames that day.

The boy's footprints were washed from the beach

by the next high tide. As the afternoon sun stretched
the shadows, Dru wandered along the damp, shining
sand near the water's edge. For a long time she
walked, to the next bay then turned back again as the
sun lowered. She caught her breath when she saw the
glint of sun on metal. There was a bike leaning against
Sea Winds' fall-about shed. Footprints crossed hers
on the damp sand and arced towards the cottonwoods.
There in the shadows, an arm hooked over a low
branch, was Locke. Waiting for her.

The breeze moved the leaves so that pale patches of
sun shimmered over his shoulders and his russet hair.
There was no sound save the whispering wind and the
gulls and the ocean. She felt like laughing and crying
at the sight of him there with the scorched, cold
remains of Sam's cottage as backdrop.

He looked weary, pale. There was stubble on his
cheeks. And a gleam in his green eyes.

'It must have been hell,' she said, wanting to run to
him but held back by all that had happened.

'It was.'

'I'm so sorry, Locke. Will Eric be all right?'

'He's agreed to have treatment. There's a place in
the country—it's—nice,' he said and she tried to
imagine the trauma of committing your brother to a
place no matter how nice. 'Vanessa's sticking with
him. I don't know if that's good or bad. She was
damned irresponsible but she says she loves him so
maybe it will work out.' He sighed, flexed his
shoulders. 'It was staring me in the face—but in this
business, so many people live like Eric—act the whole
star bit. If anything, it was me who was unnatural.
Sometimes I'd joke about him playing the Ransome
Man and he'd just grin and say, "Someone's got to do
it." I never dreamed he was obsessed with it——'

'He's your brother. Sometimes it's harder to see
things like that in someone so familiar.'

'You tried to tell me.'

'I only knew half of it myself then.'

'Will you hate him for it, Dru?'

'Will you?'

He shook his head. 'I did for a few minutes when I realised what he'd almost done—but no, I can't hate him.'

'Neither can I.'

He looked around at the ruins of Sam's house then back at her.

'My mother left me a letter,' he said at last in a husky voice. 'Three pages of it. She told me a lot of things I should have seen for myself. About my dreams of Eva and what interpretation you put on them . . . three pages.' He took a slip of paper from his shirt pocket. 'But everything I needed to know was in yours.'

'I kept it brief,' she said. The words croaked out.

'One line,' his eyes skimmed it, 'The greatest line I'll ever read.'

Waiting for you at Sea Winds. I love you, she'd written.

She ran to him then as he came for her. Her bare feet lifted from the sandy ground as Locke pulled her into his arms. 'I love you, Dru,' he said and though the words were muffled in her hair, they rang clear as a bell in her head. Holding him she spilled it all out— Eva, her hurt pride that made her flaunt Michael, her failure to believe Locke could love her.

'I knew you felt obliged to do something about me because of Sam and then, when the press started making my life a misery I thought you felt responsible and as you wanted a wife anyway just to stop tongues wagging——'

He laughed. 'I did feel responsible. Because I *was*. I was so damned frustrated. You were letting me think that you might get back together with Pennington and he sounded all wrong for you. All I had to do I thought, was sit back and wait for the press to link your name with mine and that would put him off and keep you unattached until November.'

'You mean you really intended coming back?'

'Oh yes. A few months I thought, to let you get your boyfriend out of your system and I'd come and sweep you off your feet. Instead after Sam died you started talking about going back to Pennington and all my plans fell apart.'

'But I only said that because I was sure Sam had asked you to keep an eye on me and I didn't want you to feel obliged.'

'Well, how was I to know that? Anyway I thought I had it licked with the press ferreting out juicy bits about any girl I ever speak to. But the very time I wanted them to find out they milled around like a lot of sheep. So I had to leak your name as my mistress.'

'*You* told them?'

'Very uncharacteristic of me. Then there was that day here when I'd read about Pennington's engagement and thought that all your talk of making up with him had been sheer pride and I'd got you involved with the press for nothing. And you cried and I thought you still loved him and I felt like killing him. Because then I had to sweep you off your feet before you were ready and without saying I loved you.'

'I wish you had.'

'Sheer ego, I suppose,' he confessed, 'I didn't want to start off at a disadvantage. I knew you were fond of me, knew I could make you want me, but I wanted you to love me. That's why I held back—tried to hold back—on the physical bit, to give you time. In the past I've never denied myself sexually. To wait for you was a—way of loving you I suppose. A way of saying you weren't like the other women I'd known.'

She was moved. 'You're some guy. I'm glad you

turned up and grabbed me in the dark that night even if you did scare me to death.'

'I promise not to do that again.'

'What—grab me in the dark?'

'Mmmm—well, I promise not to scare you——'

She laughed. 'Locke, what *did* Sam ask of you?'

'I'm afraid I lied to you about that. He knew I was interested in you—made me promise not to er—seduce you. Very frank he was. Marriage or nothing he told me. I agreed. Marriage I said.'

'After just two weeks?'

'How long does it take to recognise your other half?'

She gulped. 'That promise must have made Sam very happy.'

'It did,' Locke said softly, 'He fixed me with those fierce eyes and said "Aaagh." I wanted to tell you the day we were married that we had his blessing.'

She pressed into his arms and shed a few tears on his shoulder at that. For a long time they held each other until happiness bubbled up through the memories.

'You know I think I really fell for you on your second night here,' Dru linked her hands about his neck, '—when I went to bed with you.'

'Went to——?' he stopped, thought a bit. 'I *thought* you were less caustic the next morning—and my door was open—was it the dream?'

'Yes. You cried out Eva's name and I went to you. Even then I wondered how important she was to you that you had nightmares about her. Later when I knew she was your wife I assumed you dreamed of her loss because you still loved her.'

'Eva was—well, I won't ever forget her. But I stopped mourning her long ago. But the way she died ... I suppose deep down I can't shake the feeling that if I hadn't been late—oh I know, it's a pointless exercise. When I came up here I didn't realise it but I was at a crisis point in my career. Eva and I had always talked about the kind of work I desperately wanted to do—the roles I would play for nothing, just for the privilege of doing them. It occurred to me occasionally over the past years that Eva wouldn't recognise the man I'd become—a wealthy pin-up instead of an actor. Maybe that's what started me dreaming of her again. A reminder of the ideals I'd begun with and lost somewhere along the way. It was my fault, not Eric's that my career galloped off in one direction. I let him do so much for me, too much. My laziness gave him a certain control. From now on it will be different.' He rested his chin on her head. 'You know I just can't forgive myself.'

'For being lazy?'

'No, not that. For not waking up when I had you in bed with me . . .' He shook his head.

'Yes, you were pretty tame for a sex symbol.'

'I'm only tame when I'm asleep.'

'Glad to hear it.'

'Hussy. I think the stars are right about you.'

'What stars? Rock stars, film stars——?'

'Philomena's stars. She finished your chart and delivered it to the apartment. Had a long talk to Mrs Curtis who was very impressed, I hear. Philomena is doing her chart now. I read yours on the plane.'

'And it said I was a hussy?'

'More kindly worded than that. "A woman who can constantly surprise—even shock others," it said. But I knew that. "A commonsense person with a passionate nature. A sensuous woman . . .,"' he leered. 'But I knew that too.'

'Know it all.'

'You're going to have three children and be very happy.'

'Oh good.'

'—later in life you could become a celebrity——'

'I'm already a celebrity. I'm married to you.'

'—in your own right. Philomena says your stars show you becoming well known—being interviewed, writing things——'

She kissed the base of his neck. 'I'm going to be busy.'

'You will love one man all your life——'

'*I* knew that.'

'—and through troubled times you will hold on to what you love because——'

'I know. I have the pincer,' she took a Philomena grip on his arm and he pretended agony.

'I hope that part is right,' he said, suddenly serious, 'It isn't easy keeping a marriage alive in my business. Even without the Ransome image I'll still be photographed with actresses and the studios and papers will want to make a romance between me and every leading lady . . .'

'We'll be like Mr and Mrs Newman and Mr and Mrs Heston. They survived.'

'There'll be weeks and weeks of location work.'

'I'll get a passport.'

'And how will you feel about seeing me make love to some other woman on the screen?'

'Smug.'

'An answer for everything,' he marvelled.

'Not everything.' She looked around at the lonely stretch of beach. 'What about this place Locke? I don't think I could bear to see a club and carpark over there changing everything.'

'Let's wait and see. It could take years.'

Years. And they would be together. Things change, Sam had said. Perhaps she wouldn't need to cling to this place of time-standing-still anymore.

'I suppose it's too much to ask that you've got some champagne on ice?' he murmured in her ear.

'I've got *the* champagne on ice. And two glasses that have been frosted over for days.'

'Does that mean you're offering me a room for the night again?'

'It looks like it. And this time you won't have to sleep with the baggage.'

'I have every intention of sleeping with the baggage . . .'

'Oh! You——' She bounced her fist off his shoulder.

Her letter was plucked fluttering from his pocket and carried away. Up and up where the breeze whispered Sam's old name for her in the cottonwood trees. You see Sam, it all turned out.

The sea rolled and retreated and Dru thought of an April night when Locke had kissed her under a million stars. He held her close now, rubbing his cheek against hers. Then he kissed her and the earth tilted as it was meant to. Dru put a hand to her tingling face as they began to walk across the dunes to Sea Winds.

'You might have shaved,' she said.

Mills & Boon

Take 4
Exciting Books
Absolutely
FREE

Love, romance, intrigue... all are captured for you by
Mills & Boon's top-selling authors. By becoming a
regular reader of Mills & Boon's Romances you can
enjoy 6 superb new titles every month plus a whole
range of special benefits: your very own personal
membership card, a free monthly newsletter packed
with recipes, competitions, exclusive book offers and
a monthly guide to the stars, plus extra bargain offers
and big cash savings.

**AND an Introductory FREE GIFT for YOU.
Turn over the page for details.**

As a special introduction we will send you four
exciting Mills & Boon Romances Free and
without obligation when you complete
and return this coupon.

At the same time we will reserve a subscription to
Mills & Boon Reader Service for you. Every month,
you will receive 6 of the very latest novels by leading
Romantic Fiction authors, delivered direct to your
door. You don't pay extra for delivery — postage and
packing is always completely Free. There is no
obligation or commitment — you can cancel your
subscription at any time.

You have nothing to lose and a whole world of
romance to gain.

Just fill in and post the coupon today to **MILLS & BOON
READER SERVICE, FREEPOST, P.O. BOX 236, CROYDON,
SURREY CR9 9EL.**

Please Note:- **READERS IN SOUTH AFRICA write to
Mills & Boon, Postbag X3010,
Randburg 2125, S. Africa.**

FREE BOOKS CERTIFICATE

**To: Mills & Boon Reader Service, FREEPOST, P.O. Box 236,
Croydon, Surrey CR9 9EL.**

Please send me, free and without obligation, four Mills & Boon Romances, and reserve a
Reader Service Subscription for me. If I decide to subscribe I shall, from the beginning of the
month following my free parcel of books, receive six new books each month for £6.60, post
and packing free. If I decide not to subscribe, I shall write to you within 10 days. The free
books are mine to keep in any case. I understand that I may cancel my subscription at any
time simply by writing to you. I am over 18 years of age.

Please write in BLOCK CAPITALS.

Signature _____

Name _____

Address _____

_____ Post code _____

SEND NO MONEY — TAKE NO RISKS.

Please don't forget to include your Postcode.

*Remember, postcodes speed delivery. Offer applies in UK only and is not valid
to present subscribers. Mills & Boon reserve the right to exercise discretion in
granting membership. If price changes are necessary you will be notified.*

6R   Offer expires 31st December 1985

EP86

ROMANCE

Variety is the spice of romance

Each month, Mills & Boon publish new romances. New stories about people falling in love. A world of variety in romance — from the best writers in the romantic world. Choose from these titles in November.

RETURN TO WALLABY CREEK Kerry Allyne
PILLOW PORTRAITS Rosemary Carter
THE DRIFTWOOD DRAGON Ann Charlton
TO CAGE A WHIRLWIND Jane Donnelly
A MAN WORTH KNOWING Alison Fraser
INJURED INNOCENT Penny Jordan
TOUCH NOT MY HEART Leigh Michaels
SWEET AS MY REVENGE Susan Napier
SOUTH SEAS AFFAIR Kay Thorpe
DANGER ZONE Madeleine Ker
***THE GARLAND GIRL** Liza Manning
***MacBRIDE OF TORDARROCH** Essie Summers

On sale where you buy paperbacks. If you require further information or have any difficulty obtaining them, write to: Mills & Boon Reader Service, PO Box 236, Thornton Road, Croydon, Surrey CR9 3RU, England.

*These two titles are available *only* from Mills & Boon Reader Service.

Mills & Boon
the rose of romance